Bond
No.1 for exam success

English
Assessment Papers

10-11+ years

Book 2

OXFORD
UNIVERSITY PRESS

OXFORD
UNIVERSITY PRESS

Great Clarendon Street, Oxford, OX2 6DP, United Kingdom

Oxford University Press is a department of the University of Oxford.
It furthers the University's objective of excellence in research,
scholarship, and education by publishing worldwide. Oxford is a
registered trade mark of Oxford University Press in the UK and in
certain other countries

British Library Cataloguing in Publication Data
Data available

978-0-19-274006-9

10 9 8 7 6

Paper used in the production of this book is a natural, recyclable
product made from wood grown in sustainable forests.
The manufacturing process conforms to the environmental
regulations of the country of origin.

Printed in China

Acknowledgements

The publishers would like to thank the following for permissions to
use copyright material:

Page make-up: OKS Prepress, India
Illustrations: Lisa Smith (Sylvie Poggio Artists Agency)
Cover illustrations: Lo Cole

Pp 3–4 extract from *Kensuke's Kingdom* by Michael Morpurgo, copyright © 1999
Michael Morpurgo. Published by Egmont Books, reproduced by permission of
David Higham Associates; pp9–10 'Greens never tasted so good' by Rebecca
Smithers, in the *Guardian* 21 November 2006. Copyright Guardian News and
Media Ltd 2006; p15 'George' from *Complete Verse* by Hilaire Belloc. Copyright
© The Estate of Hilaire Belloc 1970. Reproduced by Peters Fraser & Dunlop on
behalf of the Estate of Hilaire Belloc; pp27–28 'Captain Scott – Antarctic
Explorer', extract from the National Maritime Museum website; pp38–39
extract from *Long Walk to Freedom* by Nelson Mandela, Copyright © Nelson
Rolihlahla Mandela 2001. Reprinted by permission of Little, Brown and
Company; pp44–45 extract from *The No. 1 Ladies' Detective Agency* by Alexander
McCall Smith, copyright © Alexander McCall Smith 1999. Published by Birlinn,
reprinted by permissions of David Higham Associates; pp50–51 extract from
A Walk for Jim by Sally Thomas, Copyright © Sally Thomas 2001; pp57–58
extract from *Blitzcat* by Robert Westall © The Estate of Robert Westall 1994.
Published by HarperCollins, reprinted by permission of Laura Cecil Agency.

Although we have made every effort to trace and contact all
copyright holders before publication this has not been possible in all
cases. If notified, the publisher will rectify any errors or omissions at
the earliest opportunity.

Links to third party websites are provided by Oxford in good faith
and for information only. Oxford disclaims any responsibility for
the materials contained in any third party website referenced in
this work.

Before you get started

What is Bond?

This book is part of the Bond Assessment Papers series for English, which provides **thorough and continuous practice of key English skills** from ages five to thirteen. Bond's English resources are ideal preparation for Key Stage 1 and Key Stage 2 SATs, the 11+ and other selective school entrance exams.

How does the scope of this book match real exam content?

English 10-11+ Book 1 and *Book 2* are the core Bond 11+ books. Each paper is **pitched at the level of a typical 11+ exam** and practises comprehension, spelling, grammar and vocabulary work. The papers are also in line with other selective exams for this age group. The coverage is matched to the National Curriculum and the National Literacy Strategy and will also **provide invaluable preparation for Key Stage 2 SATs**. It is outside the scope of this book to practise extended and creative writing skills. *Bond Focus on Writing* provides full coverage of writing skills.

What does the book contain?

- **10 papers** – each one contains 100 questions.

- **Tutorial links throughout** – 📖 – this icon appears in the margin next to the questions. It indicates links to the relevant section in *How to do … 11+ English*, our invaluable subject guide that offers explanations and practice for all core question types.

- **Scoring devices** – there are score boxes in the margins and a Progress Chart on page 64. The chart is a visual and motivating way for children to see how they are doing. It also turns the score into a percentage that can help decide what to do next.

- **Next Steps Planner** – advice on what to do after finishing the papers can be found on the inside back cover.

- **Answers** – located in an easily-removed central pull-out section.

How can you use this book?

One of the great strengths of Bond Assessment Papers is their flexibility. They can be used at home, in school and by tutors to:

- **set timed formal practice tests** – allow about 50 minutes per paper in line with standard 11+ demands. Reduce the suggested time limit by five minutes to practise working at speed

- provide **bite-sized chunks** for regular practice

- **highlight strengths and weaknesses** in the core skills

- identify **individual needs**

- set **homework**

- follow **a complete 11+ preparation strategy** alongside *The Parents' Guide to the 11+* (see below).

It is best to start at the beginning and work through the papers in order. If you are using the book as part of a careful run-in to the 11+, we suggest that you also have four other essential Bond resources close at hand:

How to do 11+ English: the subject guide that explains all the question types practised in this book. Use the cross-reference icons to find the relevant sections.

Focus on Comprehension: the practical handbook that clearly shows children how to read and understand the text, understand the questions and assess their own answers.

Focus on Writing: the essential resource that explains the key components of successful writing.

The Parents' Guide to the 11+: the step-by-step guide to the whole 11+ experience. It clearly explains the 11+ process, provides guidance on how to assess children, helps you to set complete action plans for practice and explains how you can use *English 10-11+ Book 1* and *Book 2* as part of a strategic run-in to the exam.

See the inside front cover for more details of these books.

What does a score mean and how can it be improved?

It is unfortunately impossible to guarantee that a child will pass the 11+ exam if they achieve a certain score on any practice book or paper. Success on the day depends on a host of factors, including the scores of the other children sitting the test. However, we can give some guidance on what a score indicates and how to improve it.

If children colour in the Progress Chart on page 64, this will give an idea of present performance in percentage terms. The Next Steps Planner inside the back cover will help you to decide what to do next to help a child progress. It is always valuable to go over wrong answers with children. If they are having trouble with any particular question type, follow the tutorial links to *How to do ... 11+ English* for step-by-step explanations and further practice.

Don't forget the website ...!

Visit www.bond11plus.co.uk for lots of advice, information and suggestions on everything to do with Bond, the 11+ and helping children to do their best.

Key words

Some special words are used in this book. You will find them in **bold** each time they appear in the Papers. These words are explained here.

abbreviation	a word or words which are shortened
abstract noun	a word referring to a concept or idea *love*
active verb	when the main person or thing does the action *he took it*
adjectival phrase	a group of words describing a noun
adjective	a word that describes somebody or something
adverb	a word that gives extra meaning to a verb
adverbial phrase	a word or phrase that makes the meaning of a verb, adjective or another adverb more specific, e.g. The Cheshire cat vanished *quite slowly,* beginning with the end of its tail
alphabetical order	words arranged in the order found in the alphabet
antonym	a word with a meaning opposite to another word *hot – cold*
clause	a section of a sentence with a verb
collective noun	a word referring to a group *swarm*
complex sentence	a sentence containing a main clause and subordinate clause(s)
compound word	a word made up of two other words *football*
conditional	a clause or sentence expressing the idea that one thing depends on another
conjunction	a word used to link sentences, phrases or words *and, but*
connective	a word or words that join clauses or sentences
contraction	two words shortened into one with an apostrophe placed where the letter/s have been dropped *do not = don't*
definition	meanings of words
diminutive	a word implying smallness *booklet*
fronted adverbial	an adverbial that has been moved before the verb, e.g. *The day after tomorrow,* I'm going on holiday
homophone	words that have the same sound as another but a different meaning or spelling *right/write*
main clause	a clause in a sentence which makes sense on its own
metaphor	a figurative expression in which something is described in terms usually associated with another *the sky is a sapphire sea*
modal verb	verbs that change the meaning of other verbs, e.g. can, will
noun	a word for somebody or something
object	a noun referring to a person or thing which is affected by the action of a verb *He ate an ice cream*
onomatopoeic	a word that echoes a sound, associated with its meaning *hiss*
parenthesis	this is a word or phrase that is separated off from the main sentence by brackets, commas or dashes usually because it contains additional information not essential to its understanding
passive verb	when the main person or thing has the action done to it *it was taken by him*
past tense	something that has already happened
phrase	a group of words that act as a unit
plural	more than one *cats*
prefix	a group of letters added to the beginning of a word *un, dis*
preposition	a word that relates other words to each other *the book on the table*
pronoun	a word used to replace a noun
proper noun	the name of a person, place, etc. *Ben*
relative clause	a special type of subordinate clause that makes the meaning of a noun more specific, e.g. The prize *that I won* was a book
reported speech	what has been said without using the exact words or speech marks

root word	words to which prefixes or suffixes can be added to make other words *quickly*
simile	an expression to describe what something is like *as cold as ice*
singular	one *cat*
subject	the person or thing who does the action expressed by the verb *the lion roared*
subordinate clause	gives more information about and is dependent on the main clause
suffix	a group of letters added to the end of a word *ly, ful*
superlative	describes the limit of a quality (adjective or adverb) *most/least* or *shortest*
synonym	a word with the same or very similar meaning to another word *quick – fast*
verb	a 'doing' or 'being' word

It is so dark out there. Black. Stella's barking. She's up by the bow. She hasn't got her harness clipped on.

Those were the last words I [Michael] ever wrote in my log. After that it's just empty pages.

I tried calling Stella first, but she wouldn't come. So I left the wheel and went forward to bring her back. I took the ball with me to sweeten her in, tempt her away from the bow of the boat.

I crouched down. 'Come on, Stella,' I said, rolling the ball from hand to hand. 'Come and get the ball.' I felt the boat turn a little in the wind, and I knew then I shouldn't have left the wheel. The ball rolled away from me quite suddenly. I lunged after it, but it was gone over the side before I could grab it. I lay there on the deck watching it bob away into the darkness. I was furious with myself for being so silly.

I was still cursing myself when I thought I heard the sound of singing. Someone was singing out there in the darkness. I called out but no one replied. So that was what Stella had been barking at.

I looked again for my ball, but by now it had disappeared. That ball had been very precious to me, precious to all of us. I knew then I had just lost a great deal more than a football.

I was angry with Stella. The whole thing had been her fault. She was still barking. I couldn't hear the singing any more. I called her again, whistled her in. She wouldn't come. I got to my feet and went forward. I took her by the collar and pulled. She would not be moved. I couldn't drag her all the way back, so I bent down to pick her up. She was still reluctant. Then I had her in my arms, but she was struggling.

I heard the wind above me in the sails. I remember thinking: this is silly, you haven't got your safety harness on, you haven't got your lifejacket on, you shouldn't be doing this. Then the boat veered violently and I was thrown sideways. With my arms full I had no time to grab the guard rail. We were in the cold of the sea before I could even open my mouth to scream.

The terrors came fast, one upon another. The lights of the *Peggy Sue* went away into the dark of the night, leaving me alone in the ocean, alone with the certainty that they were already too far away, that my cries for help could not possibly be heard. I thought then of the sharks cruising the black water beneath me – scenting me, already searching me out, homing in on me – and I knew there could be no hope. I would be eaten alive. Either that or I would drown slowly. Nothing could save me.

I trod water, frantically searching the impenetrable darkness about me for something, anything to swim towards. There was nothing.

Then a sudden glimpse of white in the sea. The breaking of a wave perhaps. But there were no waves. Stella! It had to be. I was so thankful, so relieved not to be all alone. I called out and swam towards her. She would keep bobbing away from me, vanishing, reappearing, then vanishing again. She had seemed so near, but it

5

10

15

20

25

30

35

40

took several minutes of hard swimming before I came close enough to reach out and touch her. Only then did I realise my mistake. Stella's head was mostly black. This was white. It was my football. I grabbed it and clung on, feeling the unexpected and wonderful buoyancy of it. I held on, treading water and calling for Stella. There was no answer. I called and called. But every time I opened my mouth now, the seawater washed in. I had to give her up. I had to save myself if I could.

45

From Kensuke's Kingdom by Michael Morpurgo

Underline the correct answers.

1 Why was the log in the passage the last written by Michael?

(he couldn't think what else to write, his log book fell off the boat,

he fell off the boat)

2 Why did Michael take the ball to the bow of the boat?

(to coax Stella away from the bow, to play a game with Stella,

to put it out of the way)

3 Why does Michael think Stella was barking?

(she'd seen something in the water, she'd heard what she thought was singing,

she was playing a game with him)

3

Answer these questions.

4–5 In lines 9–10 Michael states 'I knew then I shouldn't have left the wheel'. What made him think this and why?

_____

_____

6 What could the singing have been?

_____

7 Why was Michael angry with Stella?

_____

8 On falling in the water, what was Michael's biggest fear?

_____

9 What is the meaning of 'impenetrable' on line 36?

_____

4

10–12 Pick out three pieces of evidence that tell the reader how Michael felt after falling off the *Peggy Sue*.

_____

_____

_____

13 What sort of weather is suggested by the passage?

_____

14–15 Look again at the final sentence. Explain two ways you would go about doing this if you were in Michael's place.

_____

_____

12

Write a **synonym** for the words in bold.

D 9

16 The fence needed to be **strengthened**.   _____

17 The road was **blocked** with traffic.   _____

18 Will you **look after** my baby?   _____

19 The cheese was **ready to eat**.   _____

20 The **brother and sister** usually got on well.   _____

21 The constant howling wind made the dogs feel **anxious**.   _____

22 Her **description** of events was different.   _____

7

Add the missing commas to these sentences.

D 4

23–24 Hard white plaster covered the lower part of his leg, his foot, his right arm and shoulder!

25–28 We had to walk down the hill, catch the bus, jump on a train and walk up the street, just to get to Uncle Matt's house.

29–31 We were so excited we were having a picnic with crusty bread sandwiches, glistening pork pies, crunchy apples, sparkling drinks and piles of chocolate bars.

9

Complete these words with *cious* or *tious*.

E 2

32 vi_____   **33** cau_____

34 mali_____   **35** ambi_____

5

36 nutri_____

37 pre_____

38 deli_____

39 suspi_____

In each space write the most suitable **adverb**. Each word may be used only once.

immediately   tearfully   thoroughly   frantically

hysterically   slowly   peacefully

40 The kittens slept _____ next to the open fire.

41 Nina felt _____ unwell.

42 The twins laughed _____ as their dad slipped in the mud.

43 The tower had been _____ toppling over for decades.

44 Wang Ling sat up, saw her new book by her bed and _____ started to read.

45 Ben _____ swam to the surface of the water.

46 As Bola's grandparents left he _____ said good-bye.

Circle the masculine words.

47–51   niece   ewe   (lord)   sow

boar   (men)   doe   bull

(duke)   wife

Rewrite these sentences without double negatives.

52 There weren't no clouds in the sky.

_____

53 Kate hadn't done no homework.

_____

54 There isn't no water for the dog to drink.

_____

Write two sentences that indicate **parenthesis** using brackets, commas or dashes.

55 _____

_____

56 _____

_____

Write *their*, *there* or *they're* in each gap.

57–58 If we don't hurry _____ going to be late for _____ train.

59–60 _____ boots are _____.

61–63 Over _____ _____ working very hard on _____ paintings.

64–65 Look over _____, it looks like _____ cat has fallen in the pond!

Rewrite the passage correctly, starting a new line when a different person starts to speak.

66–82 Go and sit down both of you the teacher ordered But ... I tried to explain as we made our way to our desks Now get on with your work the dreaded voice said No more cheating or insolence I want you to sit in your seats take out your books and start reading

_____

_____

_____

_____

_____

Write **active** or **passive** next to each sentence.

83 Ellen grabbed the ball and ran. _____

84 The cows walked slowly across the field. _____

85 Daniel was knocked out of the tree. _____

86 The cars raced around the track. _____

Add a **clause** to each of these to make a longer sentence. Use a different **connective** each time.

D 2
D 6

87–88 The water rose quickly, cutting off our exit _____

_____

89–90 The water rose quickly, cutting off our exit _____

_____

91–92 The water rose quickly, cutting off our exit _____

_____

6

E 2

Rewrite the misspelt words correctly.

93 parlament	_____	**94** pronuncation	_____	
95 recomend	_____	**96** musle	_____	
97 aparent	_____	**98** comunicate	_____	
99 frequantly	_____	**100** atached	_____	8

Greens never tasted so good

Janet Parkinson, head of Howarth Primary School near Bradford, in Yorkshire, sums
up Steve Thorpe in just one word: 'He's ... wow!' Steve, who has two daughters
at the school, works full-time as a gardener with the local council and nearly five
years ago set up an after-school gardening club at the school, initially as a way of
resolving some vandalism problems in the town.   5

Flowers and plants were grown and used to smarten up the town centre, and the
vandalism stopped. The project has gone from strength to strength and is now not
only central to food and other education in the school, but has led to closer links
with the local community.

Now 40 regular members of Steve's popular after-school gardening club (another   10
eager 20 pupils are on a waiting list) plant and tend the vegetables, while the whole
school (260 pupils plus 45 in the nursery) regularly gets involved in harvesting
the vegetables, shelling peas and peeling potatoes in the school kitchen and then
eating their efforts for their school lunches.

Over the past year, the range of vegetables served up at lunchtime has included   15
peas, tomatoes, lettuce, cucumber, peppers, runner beans, carrots, leeks, potatoes,
Brussels sprouts, cabbage and beetroot. Produce has been entered into local

horticultural shows – winning trophy after trophy for the youngsters. The school has won three 'Yorkshire in Bloom' plaudits.

Thorpe is now one of four individuals shortlisted for one of the Soil Association's *20* prestigious annual school food awards, due to be presented on Thursday by chef Jamie Oliver and the association's school meals policy advisor, Jeanette Orrey, at a ceremony in Birmingham.

… The school food hero award recognises one individual who has worked hard to make a difference to school meals in their area. *25*

Steve, now also a parent governor, is modest about his achievements. He says: 'For me the most satisfying part is the vegetable gardening, because now I feel that the whole school is involved, and growing is there in the curriculum, too. Many of these children thought vegetables came straight out of plastic bags, not the ground.' The community has also benefited, and the grateful local police have donated plant- *30* pots, because the gardening club maintains their flowers.

If Steve wins the award, the school will receive £1,000. And his priority for the money? It has been earmarked to pay for the much-needed extension of the school's greenhouse …

From an article in the *Guardian* by Rebecca Smithers

Underline the correct answers.

1 How long has the school gardening club been running?

(less than five years, five years, more than five years)

2 How many children are or would like to be involved in the school gardening club?

(40, 45, 60)

3 The school food hero award is provided by which organisation?

(Yorkshire County Council, The Soil Association, Howarth Primary School)

3

Answer these questions.

4 Why is Janet Parkinson so impressed with Steve Thorpe?

_____

5–7 Detail three benefits the gardening club has had for Howarth Primary School.

_____

_____

_____

8 Why do you think the planting of flowers and plants in the town centre helped stop the vandalism?

_____

9 What does the **phrase** 'the project has gone from strength to strength' mean (line 7)?

_____

10 Give the meaning of the word 'plaudits' (line 19) as it is used in the passage.

_____

11–12 Why is this school club about more than just the children growing and eating their own vegetables? Give two reasons.

_____

_____

13 Why do you think an extension is needed for the club's greenhouse?

_____

14–15 List two of Steve's characteristics that make him popular with both children and teachers.

_____

_____

12

Add the **suffix** _ive_ to each of these words. Don't forget any spelling changes.

E 2

16 conduct _____

17 invent _____

18 progress _____

19 cooperate _____

20 speculate _____

21 alternate _____

22 impress _____

23 offence _____

8

Add the missing commas to these sentences.

D 4

24–25 The air caught unpleasantly in his throat, nearly making him cough, then struggled into his lungs.

26–27 The voice was deep and powerful, a man's voice, though at times very quiet.

28–30 Steven watched in slow motion as the ball flew towards the house, just missing the neighbour's cat, skimmed the flowers, gently rocking the garden statue and smashed the kitchen window!

7

11

Write two **adjectives** to describe each of these **nouns**. A different word must be used each time.

31–32 _____, _____ dog

33–34 _____, _____ whistle

35–36 _____, _____ tree

Write two sentences that include a **relative clause** using the following words.

37 where

_____

38 who

_____

Write two meanings for each of these words. One might be a meaning that has evolved over recent years.

39–40 paddy

_____

_____

41–42 green

_____

_____

With a line, match the beginning of the proverb with its end.

43 More haste,   without fire.

44 First come,   in one basket.

45 There is no smoke   less speed.

46 Don't put all your eggs   flock together.

47 Birds of a feather   has a silver lining.

48 Every cloud   first served.

Choose the correct **verb** form for each of these sentences.

D 6

49 Damien (is/are) best friends with Tom and Reuben.

50 The Wren family (was/were) loving the theme park.

51 Veejay could (saw/see) that the beans had been growing.

52 Sarah (catched/caught) the ball confidently.

53 Mitchell found the homework (what/which) he'd been looking for.

54 Helen (turned/turning) her head away instinctively.

55 There (was/were) no moon and they couldn't see much.

7

Add the **suffix** to each of these words. Don't forget any spelling changes.

E 2

56 consider + able _____

57 notice + able _____

58 measure + able _____

59 response + ible _____

60 reproduce + ible _____

61 access + ible _____

62 reason + able _____

63 change + able _____

8

Punctuate these sentences correctly.

D 5

64–69 that film terrified me gulped danny

_____

70–76 meena slipped down into the fast moving river help she screamed

_____

77–86 let's eat our lunch here said jay it's warm in the sun

_____

23

Finish these **similes**, using your own words.

C 4

87 as shiny as _____

88 as black as _____

89 as fast as a _____

90 as strong as _____

4

Rewrite these statements as questions, changing as few words as possible.

91 There are fewer people in Australia than in the United Kingdom.

_____

92 We are going to the party tonight.

_____

Add a **prefix** to each of these to make a new word.

93 _____social

94 _____normal

95 _____act

96 _____scope

97 _____polite

98 _____connect

99 _____operate

100 _____circle

Now go to the Progress Chart to record your score!   Total   100

When George's Grandmamma was told
That George had been as good as Gold,
She Promised in the Afternoon
To buy him an *Immense BALLOON*.
And   5
so she did; but when it came,
It got into a candle flame,
And being of a dangerous sort
Exploded
with a loud report!   10
The Lights went out! The Windows broke!
The Room was filled with reeking smoke.
And in the darkness shrieks and yells
Were mingled with Electric Bells,
And falling masonry and groans,   15
And crunching, as of broken bones,
And dreadful shrieks, when, worst of all,
The House itself began to fall!
It tottered, shuddering to and fro,
Then crashed into the street below –   20
Which happened to be Savile Row.
When Help arrived, among the Dead
Were
Cousin Mary,
Little Fred,   25
The Footmen
(both of them),
The Groom,
The man that cleaned the Billiard Room,
The Chaplain, and   30
The Still-Room Maid.
And I am dreadfully afraid
That Monsieur Champignon, the Chef,
Will now be
permanently deaf –   35
And both his
Aides
are much the same
While George, who was in part to blame,
Received, you will regret to hear,   40
A nasty lump
behind the ear.

MORAL
The moral is that little Boys
Should not be given dangerous Toys.   45

George by Hilaire Belloc

Underline the correct answers.

1 Why was George given the balloon?

(for being strong and bold, for doing what he was told,

for being as good as gold)

2 What happened to Monsieur Champignon?

(he died, he received a nasty lump, he became deaf)

2

Answer these questions.

3 What is the meaning of the word 'Immense' on line 4?

_____

4–6 When the balloon exploded it triggered a number of events. List six of them.

_____

_____

_____

7 The poem states that George was 'in part to blame' (line 39). Why?

_____

8–10 As you read the poem you will notice that some words or **phrases** have been presented by the poet in different ways. Write two ways the poet has done this and explain why this has been done.

_____

_____

11–12 What message does the poem convey? Do you think the message is just?

_____

_____

13–15 Describe two ways the poet wanted the readers to feel when reading the poem. Use one piece of evidence from the poem to support your answer.

_____

_____

_____

13

In each sentence underline the **object** and write a **pronoun** for each **subject**.

16–17 The children played in the pool.   subject pronoun _____

18–19 The baby slept in the cot.   subject pronoun _____

20–21 Henry rode his bike to school.   subject pronoun _____

22–23 The firemen relaxed after putting out the fire.   subject pronoun _____

8

From the **verbs** listed write a **noun** ending in *ion*.

24 divide   _____   **25** invade   _____

26 explode   _____   **27** rotate   _____

28 collide   _____   **29** comprehend   _____

30 confess   _____   **31** deflect   _____

8

Use each word in a sentence to show its meaning. You can add **suffixes** to them.

32 dextrous   _____

33 conceit   _____

34 exhilarate   _____

35 persistence   _____

36 pursue   _____

37 yield   _____

6

Write the two words each **contraction** stands for.

38 we're   _____ _____

39 should've   _____ _____

40 I'll   _____ _____

41 won't   _____ _____

42 let's   _____ _____

43 shan't   _____ _____

6

Write six sentences. In each sentence use the listed phrase correctly.

44 heavy metal detectort

_____

45 heavy-metal detector

_____

46 hot water bottle

_____

47 hot-water bottle

_____

48 man eating crocodile

_____

49 man-eating crocodile

_____

Write an **antonym** for each of these words.

50 subtract	_____	**51** scream	_____
52 extend	_____	**53** least	_____
54 spectator	_____	**55** confident	_____
56 mend	_____	**57** exterior	_____

In each of these sentences a word is incorrect. Underline the word and rewrite it correctly.

58 The Stamp family can't move until the removal truck was here.

_____

59 Kyle and me went swimming.

_____

60 Darren, Wusai and I is a good team.

_____

61 The paint weren't drying quickly enough.

_____

62 Najib didn't want no tea.

_____

Underline the **root words** in each of these.

D 11

63 transmigrate

64 reintroduce

65 intersection

66 debater

67 consistent

68 resistance

69 antifreeze

70 almighty

8

Copy these sentences, adding the missing punctuation and capital letters.

D 5

71–82 quick called laura if we hurry we can catch the bus from waterloo road

_____

_____

83–89 come on then shouted anna as she raced off

_____

19

Complete the second **clause** (that includes a **verb**) for each of these sentences.

D 2

90 I read a book each night that _____

D 6

_____

91 My mum takes the bus to work _____

_____

92 I ate my supper while _____

_____

3

Write the **plural** form of these words.

E 2

93 waltz _____

94 glass _____

95 chief _____

96 scenario _____

97 identity _____

98 success _____

99 werewolf _____

100 gypsy _____

8

Now go to the Progress Chart to record your score! Total 100

Paper 4

The train had stopped before a red signal which blocked the way. The engineer and conductor were talking excitedly with a signal-man, whom the station-master at Medicine Bow, the next stopping place, had sent on before. The passengers drew around and took part in the discussion, in which Colonel Proctor, with his insolent manner, was conspicuous.

Passepartout, joining the group, heard the signal-man say, 'No! you can't pass. The bridge at Medicine Bow is shaky, and would not bear the weight of the train.'

This was a suspension-bridge thrown over some rapids, about a mile from the place they now were. According to the signal-man, it was in a ruinous condition, several of the iron wires being broken; and it was impossible to risk the passage. He did not in any way exaggerate the condition of the bridge.

Passepartout, not daring to apprise his master of what he heard, listened with set teeth, immovable as a statue.

'Hum!' cried Colonel Proctor; 'but we are not going to stay here, I imagine, and take root in the snow?'

'Colonel,' replied the conductor, 'we have telegraphed to Omaha for a train, but it is not likely that it will reach Medicine Bow in less than six hours.'

'Six hours!' cried Passepartout.

'Certainly,' returned the conductor. 'Besides, it will take us as long as that to reach Medicine Bow on foot.'

'But it is only a mile from here,' said one of the passengers.

'Yes, but it's on the other side of the river.'

'And can't we cross that in a boat?' asked the colonel.

'That's impossible. The creek is swelled by the rains. It is a rapid, and we shall have to make a circuit of ten miles to the north to find a ford.'

The colonel launched a volley of oaths, denouncing the railway company and the conductor; and Passepartout, who was furious, was not disinclined to make common cause with him. Here was an obstacle, indeed, which all his master's bank-notes could not remove …

5

10

15

20

25

Passepartout found that he could not avoid telling his master what had occurred, and, with hanging head, he was turning towards the car when the engineer … – named Forster – called out, 'Gentlemen, perhaps there is a way, after all, to get over.'

'On the bridge?' asked a passenger.

'On the bridge.'

'With our train?'

'With our train.'

Passepartout stopped short, and eagerly listened to the engineer.

'But the bridge is unsafe,' urged the conductor.

'No matter,' replied Forster; 'I think that by putting on the very highest speed we might have a chance of getting over.'

'The devil!' muttered Passepartout.

But a number of the passengers were at once attracted by the engineer's proposal, and Colonel Proctor was especially delighted, and found the plan a very feasible one. He told stories about engineers leaping their trains over rivers without bridges, by putting on full steam; and many of those present avowed themselves of the engineer's mind.

Passepartout was astounded, and, though ready to attempt anything to get over Medicine Creek, thought the experiment proposed a little too American. 'Besides,' thought he, 'there's a still more simple way, and it does not even occur to any of these people! Sir,' said he aloud to one of the passengers, 'the engineer's plan seems to me a little dangerous, but –' …

'Are you afraid?' asked Colonel Proctor.

'I afraid! Very well; I will show these people that a Frenchman can be as American as they!'

'All aboard!' cried the conductor.

'Yes, all aboard!' repeated Passepartout, and immediately. 'But they can't prevent me from thinking that it would be more natural for us to cross the bridge on foot, and let the train come after!'

But no one heard this sage reflection, nor would anyone have acknowledged its justice …

The locomotive whistled vigorously; the engineer, reversing the steam, backed the train for nearly a mile – retiring, like a jumper, in order to take a longer leap. Then, with another whistle, he began to move forward; the train increased its speed, and soon its rapidity became frightful; a prolonged screech issued from the locomotive; the piston worked up and down twenty strokes to the second. They perceived that the whole train, rushing on at the rate of a hundred miles an hour, hardly bore upon the rails at all.

And they passed over! It was like a flash. No one saw the bridge. The train leaped, so to speak, from one bank to the other, and the engineer could not stop it until it had gone five miles beyond the station. But scarcely had the train passed the river, when the bridge, completely ruined, fell with a crash into the rapids of Medicine Bow.

From *Around the World in Eighty Days* by Jules Verne

Underline the correct answers.

1 Why were the engineer and conductor talking 'excitedly'?

(because the train had broken down, because the bridge wasn't safe to cross, because the bridge had collapsed)

2 What were the weather conditions like?

(snowy, rainy, sunny)

3 What nationality was Passepartout?

(American, British, French)

3

Answer these questions.

4 What is Medicine Bow?

_____

5 The author describes the suspension bridge as being 'thrown over some rapids'. What does he mean by this?

_____

6–8 Give the meaning of the following words as they are used in the passage.

insolent (line 4)   _____

sage (line 59)   _____

perceived (line 66)   _____

9 What is meant by the **phrase** 'was not disinclined to make common cause with him' (line 27)?

_____

10–11 What is meant by 'and many of those present avowed themselves of the engineer's mind' (line 45)? Why is this significant?

_____

_____

12 What evidence in the passage is there that the group discussed the issues off the train?

_____

13 What is the train likened to in line 62?

_____

14–15 How would you describe the sort of person Colonel Proctor is, as shown in the passage? Use evidence to support your answer.

_____

_____

12

E 1

Add *ie* or *ei* to each of these to make a word.

16 p___rce   17 br___f   18 conc___ve

19 f___nt   20 w___gh   21 dec___ve

22 retr___ve   23 fr___ght   24 dec___t

9

D 6

Add a different **conjunction** to each of these sentences.

25 The animals were frightened _____ the thunder and lightning passed above them.

26 Jacob picked up his coat slowly _____ the dogs began to circle him.

27 Shahida waited for the bus _____ it started to get dark.

28 The children ran and jumped into the stream _____ they felt so hot.

29 Fran desperately wanted to meet her friends at the bike park _____ she couldn't find her helmet.

5

C 4

Complete each sentence as a **metaphor**.

30 The moon is a _____.

31 The dress is a _____.

32 The fog was a _____.

33 The fireworks were _____.

34 The sleeping cat is a _____.

35 The crashing waves are _____.

6

D 5

Copy this sentence, adding the missing punctuation and capital letters.

36–50 tom are you awake whispered emily i can't find the torch ive bought and im scared

_____

_____

_____

15

Add a **suffix** to each word.

ship   ness   hood   less

51 neighbour   _____

52 defence   _____

53 friend   _____

54 kind   _____

55 scarce   _____

56 doubt   _____

57 town   _____

Rewrite each of the following, using only two words, one of which should have an apostrophe.

58 ward reserved for men   _____

59 ball for a dog   _____

60 wheel of a car   _____

61 stable for a pony   _____

62 toy belonging to the puppy   _____

Match a word in each column to make a **compound word**.

week	pot
no	out
land	will
jack	end
print	let
in	mark
on	where
good	going

63 _____   **64** _____

65 _____   **66** _____

67 _____   **68** _____

69 _____   **70** _____

In which tense is each of these sentences written?

71 Sally fell off her bike. _____

72 The snow is covering the ground. _____

73 We went to Windsor Castle. _____

74 Melinda has her flute lesson this afternoon. _____

75 Chickens roost at night. _____

76 The firework display is at 7pm. _____

77 It rained when Uncle James got married. _____

Write two comparing **phrases** using each of these words.

Example: cautious   *less cautious,   more cautious*

78–79 reliable   _____

_____

80–81 manageable   _____

_____

82–83 visible   _____

_____

Circle the unstressed vowel in each of these words.

84 u s u a l l y	**85** l i s t e n e r	**86** b u s i n e s s
87 p e t a l	**88** v a l u a b l e	**89** t r a v e l l e r
90 c h o c o l a t e	**91** d e s p e r a t e	**92** h i s t o r y

Put these words in **alphabetical order**.

93–97 impoverish   (1) _____

impossible   (2) _____

important   (3) _____

impracticable   (4) _____

imposition   (5) _____

Write an interesting paragraph that makes use of bullet points. Write about a hobby you have.

98–100 _____

_____

_____

_____

_____

_____

_____

3

Now go to the Progress Chart to record your score!   **Total**   100

Captain Scott – Antarctic explorer

Until the end of the 19th century, only sealers and whalers had set foot on the
desolate southern land we call Antarctica. Until as late as 1820, no one had even
seen its mainland. In the 1890s however, explorers of various countries began to
compete for being the first to reach both the North and the South Poles. In 1901–04
Captain Robert Falcon Scott (1868–1912), an officer in the Royal Navy, was the first   5
person to explore Antarctica extensively by land.

Was Britain the only country trying to reach the South Pole?

No. Several expeditions from Norway, France and Germany explored Antarctica.
While Scott was sailing south on his second expedition, he heard the news that the
Norwegian, Roald Amundsen, was going to Antarctica and was likely to reach the   10
South Pole first. Although Amundsen was an experienced Arctic explorer, Scott was
determined to get there first. He laid food depots to the south early in 1911, and set
out towards the Pole on 1 November during the second summer there.

What happened on the second expedition?

Scott planned to reach the Pole from Ross Island, using ponies and three motorised   15
sledges, with a few dogs in support, then by man-hauling his sledges. The
motorised sledges failed. The ponies suffered and were put down for food (which
was expected) and the dogs went back to base camp halfway with most of the
men. This left Scott and just four companions to pull.

Did they reach the Pole?   20

Yes, they got there on 17–18 January 1912. When they arrived they found that
Amundsen and his four Norwegian companions had got there before them. Scott's
men had been beaten and, along with all the hardships of the return journey, their
morale was badly affected.

Had the two parties approached the Pole using different methods?   25

Yes, Amundsen made his base and set off from the 'Bay of Whales', on the ice-shelf
itself. This was about 100 km nearer to the Pole than Scott on Ross Island. The
Norwegians were experienced skiers and dog-drivers, who moved very fast using
52 dogs, in teams, to pull their sledges of food and essential equipment. Amundsen
also laid more depots in advance, and further south than Scott, and small ones as   30
he went. As his sledges became lighter he killed dogs to feed the others (and his
men). The British pulled the sledges themselves. Scott, who knew little about the
proper use of skis or dogs, believed this was more noble. While the Norwegians'
only aim was to reach the Pole first, Scott also made scientific observations and
collected rock samples on the way.   35

How far did they need to travel back to reach safety?

Scott and his party needed to return across the 800 miles they had already covered.
They had to get back before the middle of April, before the Antarctic winter brought
deadly freezing temperatures and constant darkness.

What happened to them?   40

They had a disastrous time. Terrible weather included blizzards and gale force
winds. They had only limited and poor food, and shortage of fuel. Eventually,
they all died. Evans died first, probably after knocking his head during a fall into a
crevasse. Oates knew he was suffering from severe frostbite in his feet, could not
go on, and did not want to slow the others down. On 17 March 1912, he left the   45
tent during a blizzard. His final words, written down by Scott, were: 'I am just going
outside, and I may be some time'. He was never seen again. The other three died
in their tent during a blizzard at the end of March. They were only 11 miles from the
food and fuel depot.

The bodies of Scott, Dr Wilson and 'Birdie' Bowers were found on 12 November.   50
They were in their sleeping bags inside a tent covered in snow. Their journals and
papers were recovered but the bodies were left, wrapped in a tent and buried under
a snow cairn.

Underline the correct answers.

1 How many expeditions did Scott make to Antarctica?

(one, two, three)

2 Which was Amundsen's native country?

(Norway, Germany, France)

3 Who got to the South Pole first?

(Scott, Amundsen, they reached it together)

Answer these questions.

4 Describe the term 'man-hauling' (line 16).

_____

5–6 In your own words describe the type of place Antarctica is.

_____

_____

7–9 Name three things Amundsen did differently that ultimately made the difference in his attempt to reach the South Pole first.

_____

_____

_____

10 Why did Scott have to return before the middle of April?

_____

11–12 Describe the sort of person Amundsen was. Use evidence from the passage to support your answer.

_____

_____

13 With reference to the first two paragraphs only, what clue do we have that Captain Scott never made it back from Antarctica?

_____

14 How did we learn about Scott's exploration of Antarctica?

_____

15 When Oates left Scott's tent on 17 March 1912 he said 'I am just going outside, and I may be some time' (lines 46–47). Why do you think he said this?

_____

12

E 2

Each of these words has an unstressed vowel missing. Rewrite the words correctly.

16 machinry _____

17 favourte _____

18 memry _____

19 jewellry _____

20 impatent _____

21 misrable _____

22 busness _____

7

E 2

Rewrite these sentences changing them from **singular** to **plural**.

23–26 The girl was riding her horse.

_____

27–29 The rabbit fled down its burrow.

_____

30–33 He saved a stamp to add to his collection.

_____

11

D 10

For the following **abbreviations**, write out the words in full.

34 DIY_____

35 p & p_____

36 Dr_____

3

D 6

Write the **nouns** in the correct columns of the table.

37–44 happiness   grass   opinion   team

gang   Harry   flame   December

common nouns	collective nouns	proper nouns	abstract nouns

8

Some questions will be answered in the children's own words. Answers to these questions are given in *italics*. Any answers that seem to be in line with these should be marked correct.

Paper 1

1 he fell off the boat
2 to coax Stella away from the bow
3 she'd heard what she thought was singing
4–5 *Michael thought that he shouldn't have left the wheel because he felt the boat start to turn in the wind. He was worried that he might get into trouble because if the wind started to move the boat, he wasn't at the wheel to steer it.*
6 *It could have been the wind.*
7 *He blamed her for the loss of his ball because if she hadn't been at the bow he wouldn't have been trying to get her back with it.*
8 sharks
9 *unable to see into or through*
10–12 *Michael felt a range of emotions. Firstly terror: 'The terrors came fast, one upon another.' He also felt alone and on discovering what he thought was Stella he was 'so relieved not to be all alone.' Finally he felt determined: 'I had to save myself if I could.' He didn't want to drown.*
13 *The weather is calm with the occasional stronger gust of wind.*
14–15 *Child's answer suggesting ways to conserve energy, stay warm, not alert sharks and keep awake, e.g. 'I would hold onto the ball because it would help me float without using up too much of my energy. I would try to determine where the boat might be and try to move in that direction.'*
16 *reinforced*
17 *congested*
18 *mind*
19 *ripe*
20 *siblings*
21 *uneasy*
22 *version*
23–24 Hard white plaster covered the lower part of his leg, his foot, his right arm and shoulder!
25–28 We had to walk down the hill, catch the bus, jump on a train and walk up the street, just to get to Uncle Matt's house.
29–31 We were so excited we were having a picnic with crusty bread sandwiches, glistening pork pies, crunchy apples, sparkling drinks and piles of chocolate bars.
32 vicious
33 cautious
34 malicious
35 ambitious
36 nutritious
37 precious
38 delicious
39 suspicious
40 peacefully
41 thoroughly
42 hysterically
43 slowly
44 immediately
45 frantically
46 tearfully
47–51 lord, boar, men, bull, duke
52 *There weren't any clouds in the sky./There were no clouds in the sky.*
53 *Kate hadn't done her homework.*
54 *There isn't any water for the dog to drink./There is no water for the dog to drink.*
55–56 Two sentences illustrating the use of brackets, commas or dashes in parenthesis, e.g. *Jess and her dog (Barney) walked five miles.*
57–58 they're, their
59–60 Their, there
61–63 there, they're, their
64–65 there, their
66–82 'Go and sit down, both of you!' the teacher ordered. 'But …' I tried to explain as we made our way to our desks.
'Now get on with your work,' the dreaded voice said. 'No more cheating or insolence! I want you to sit in your seats, take out your books and start reading.'
83 active
84 active
85 passive
86 active
87–92 *The completion of three sentences, adding a connective and clause, e.g. 'The water rose quickly, cutting off our exit, so we turned around and went back the way we'd come.'*
93 parliament
94 pronunciation
95 recommend
96 muscle
97 apparent
98 communicate
99 frequently
100 attached

Paper 2

1 less than five years
2 60
3 The Soil Association
4 *because of the huge impact he has made in her school*
5–7 *eating the food they have grown; winning trophies thus raising the school profile; providing an interesting way of learning about food; closer links with the local community*
8 *By improving the look of the town centre it has encouraged the young people to feel proud of their surroundings and therefore have less desire to vandalise it.*
9 *It continues to grow and each new task it undertakes is done well.*
10 *expression of approval, awards*
11–12 *It has also benefited the community by taking responsibility for flower displays and care around the town. It has helped to stop vandalism in the town.*

13 *Due to the fact that the club is so popular and its activities are increasing, more room is needed for the additional plants that are being cared for.*

14–15 *Answers might include his enthusiasm, his knowledge, his commitment, his modesty and his generosity.*

16 conductive
17 inventive
18 progressive
19 cooperative
20 speculative
21 alternative
22 impressive
23 offensive

24–25 The air caught unpleasantly in his throat, nearly making him cough, then struggled into his lungs.

26–27 The voice was deep and powerful, a man's voice, though at times very quiet.

28–30 Steven watched in slow motion as the ball flew towards the house, just missing the neighbour's cat, skimmed the flowers, gently rocking the garden statue and smashed the kitchen window!

31–32 *shaggy, wet*
33–34 *shrill, loud*
35–36 *tall, majestic*

37–38 Two sentences that include a relative clause using the listed words, e.g. *That's the girl who lives near my friend.*

39–40 *paddy – a field where rice is grown; a rage or temper*
41–42 *green – a colour; environmentally friendly; inexperienced*

43 More haste, less speed.
44 First come, first served.
45 There is no smoke without fire.
46 Don't put all your eggs in one basket.
47 Birds of a feather flock together.
48 Every cloud has a silver lining.
49 is
50 were
51 see
52 caught
53 which
54 turned
55 was
56 considerable
57 noticeable
58 measurable
59 responsible
60 reproducible
61 accessible
62 reasonable
63 changeable

64–69 'That film terrified me,' gulped Danny.
70–76 Meena slipped down into the fast moving river. 'Help!' she screamed.
77–86 'Let's eat our lunch here,' said Jay. 'It's warm in the sun.'
87–90 *Four similes to be completed, e.g. 'as shiny as a jewel'.*
91 Are there fewer people in Australia than in the United Kingdom?
92 Are we going to the party tonight?
93 *antisocial*
94 *abnormal*
95 *interact*
96 *microscope*
97 *impolite*
98 *disconnect*
99 *co-operate*
100 *semicircle*

Paper 3

1 for being as good as gold
2 he became deaf
3 *huge*
4–6 (1 mark = 2 events) *the lights went out; windows broke; smoke filled the room; people shrieked; loud bells sounded; masonry fell; bones were broken; the house fell down*
7 *because it was George's balloon that triggered the explosion when it came near the candle*
8–10 *The poet has used capital letters on unexpected words, italics and new lines. The poet has done this to emphasise the words (to make them stand out).*
11–12 *The message of the poem is that boys shouldn't be given dangerous toys, which is right, but a balloon isn't normally classed as a dangerous toy!*
13–15 *The poet wanted readers to be shocked because the topic of the poem, an explosion leading to people dying, is serious. This is shown by the detailed list of the effects of the explosion as well as the list of the people who died. The tone of the poem is, however, light so the poet also wanted people to be amused. This is shown in the way the people who died are named, such as 'little Fred'.*
16–17 The children played in the <u>pool</u>. subject pronoun – They
18–19 The baby slept in the <u>cot</u>. subject pronoun – He/She
20–21 Henry rode his <u>bike</u> to school. subject pronoun – He
22–23 The firemen relaxed after putting out the <u>fire</u>. subject pronoun – They
24 division
25 invasion
26 explosion
27 rotation
28 collision
29 comprehension
30 confession
31 deflection
32 *The dextrous surgeon completed another successful surgery.*
33 *People found the woman to be conceited because she talked about herself so much.*
34 *The team was exhilarated when they won the match.*
35 *It was his persistence that led him to find the rare book.*
36 *I will pursue my studies at university next year.*
37 *It is important to yield to oncoming traffic at the junction.*
38 we are
39 should have

40 I will

41 will not

42 let us

43 shall not

44–49 Each sentence using the listed phrase correctly, e.g.
a hot water bottle – a water bottle that feels hot, a hot-water bottle – a container filled with hot water to warm a bed.

50 *add*

51 *whisper*

52 *contract*

53 *most*

54 *participant*

55 *unconfident*

56 *break*

57 *interior*

58 <u>was</u>   is

59 <u>me</u>   I

60 <u>is</u>   are

61 <u>weren't</u>   wasn't

62 <u>no</u>   any

63 trans<u>migrate</u>

64 <u>re</u>introduce

65 inter<u>section</u>

66 <u>debate</u>r

67 <u>consist</u>ent

68 <u>resist</u>ance

69 <u>antifreeze</u>

70 al<u>mighty</u>

71–82 'Quick!' called Laura. 'If we hurry we can catch the bus from Waterloo Road.'

83–89 'Come on then,' shouted Anna, as she raced off.

90–92 *Second clauses added to the beginning of sentences provided. A clause must include a verb, e.g. 'I read a book each night that terrified me before I went to sleep.'*

93 waltzes

94 glasses

95 chiefs

96 scenarios

97 identities

98 successes

99 werewolves

100 gypsies

Paper 4

1 because the bridge wasn't safe to cross

2 snowy

3 French

4 *the next place the train was to stop/a town/a train station*

5 *The author uses this description to highlight to the reader that the bridge was originally built hastily and with little care, hence it is now unsafe to cross.*

6–8 insolent – *insulting*
sage – *prudent, wise*
perceived – *believed, became aware of*

9 *that Passepartout tended to agree with the colonel*

10–11 *Many of the passengers declared openly that they felt the engineer's plan was a good one. The more*

people that believed it was a good idea and said so, the more others would be persuaded without possibly thinking through the consequences.

12 *Towards the end of the passage the conductor cries 'All aboard!'.*

13 *an athlete/a long jumper*

14–15 *Colonel Proctor can be described as an overbearing, dominating and loud person, e.g. 'Colonel Proctor is quite loud and enjoys being the centre of attention. This is shown when, after the engineer has made his proposal, the colonel begins to tell stories about trains leaping over rivers without bridges.'*

16 pierce

17 brief

18 conceive

19 feint

20 weigh

21 deceive

22 retrieve

23 freight

24 deceit

25 *as/when*

26 *while/as*

27 *until*

28 *because*

29 *but*

30–35 *Each metaphor completed correctly, where an object is described in terms usually associated with another object, e.g. The crashing waves are a raging bull.*

36–50 'Tom, are you awake?' whispered Emily. 'I can't find the torch I've bought and I'm scared.'

51 neighbourhood

52 defenceless

53 friendship

54 kindness

55 scarceness

56 doubtless

57 township

58 men's ward

59 dog's ball

60 car's wheel

61 pony's stable

62 puppy's toy

63–70 weekend, nowhere, landmark, jackpot, printout, inlet, ongoing, goodwill

71 past

72 present

73 past

74 future

75 present

76 future

77 past

78–79 *least reliable, most reliable*

80–81 *less manageable, more manageable*

82–83 *least visible, most visible*

84 u s u @ l l y

85 l i s t @ n e r

86 b u s i n e s s

87 p e t @ l

88 v a l u @ b l e

89 t r a v @ l l e r

90 choc◎late

91 desp◎rate

92 hist◎ry

93–97 (1) important (2) imposition (3) impossible
(4) impoverish (5) impracticable

98–100 A short paragraph illustrating the correct use of bullet
points.

Paper 5

1 two

2 Norway

3 Amundsen

4 *to move a thing using human effort*

5–6 *barren, deserted, dismal, challenging, cold,
dangerous, etc.*

7–9 *Amundsen started closer to the Pole; he had a more
experienced team; he laid more food depots; he
concentrated on being first to the Pole and didn't
collect samples and make observations on the way.*

10 *Scott had to return before the winter with its freezing
temperatures and constant darkness set in.*

11–12 *Amundsen was an organised, skilled explorer who
had courage and determination. His skill as an
explorer is shown in the way he set out more but
smaller food depots as he knew what to expect and
what his team would need.*

13 *the date Scott set off on the expedition and the date
he died*

14 *from his journals*

15 *Oates realised he was going to die and wanted to do
so away from the others hence stating 'I may be some
time' but really knowing he would never return.*

16 machinery

17 favourite

18 memory

19 jewellery

20 impatient

21 miserable

22 business

23–26 The girls were riding their horses.

27–29 The rabbits fled down their burrows.

30–33 They saved the stamps to add to their collections.

34 Do it yourself

35 postage and packaging

36 Doctor

37–44 common nouns – grass, flame
collective nouns – team, gang
proper nouns – Harry, December
abstract nouns – happiness, opinion

45 avoided

46 improving

47 repeatedly

48 inverted

49 Recently

50 return

51 pedestrian

52–61 As Zoe and Rupa slept soundly strange things began
to happen. A Night to Remember, the book Rupa
had been reading, suddenly fell open at a page. The
page told the story of a ghost which haunted the
streets of Skegness every Thursday night.

62–63 *loving, lovely*

64–65 *clearly, cleared*

66–67 *cyclist, cycling*

68–69 *payment, paying*

70 official

71 financial

72 special

73 partial

74 confidential

75 commercial

76 essential

77–78 Wes thought that he must have been dreaming.

79–80 My Dad collapsed into his chair because the run had
exhausted him!

81–82 The picture fell from the wall, glass smashing
everywhere.

83–84 Judy wondered whether the book might be useful for
her project.

85 *in answer to your letter*

86 *a form can be got from*

87 *if you want to come*

88 *we are letting you know*

89–94 'Where is Jess,' moaned Dad. 'We really need to get
going or we will miss our ferry.' / 'She is coming, I
can hear her racing down the stairs,' replied Mum. /
'About time too!' continued Dad. / As Jess climbed
into the car, Mum enquired, 'Have you got your
coat?' / 'Oops ... shall I go and get it?' Jess asked. /
'Yes and be VERY quick,' Dad almost shouted, 'I'm
losing my patience!' / 'Sorry,' she called as she flew
into the house.

95 (3)

96 (2)

97 (1)

98 (3)

99 (1)

100 (2)

Paper 6

1 Ireland

2 Pat

3 winter

4–5 *because she had died or because she had asked him
to leave*

6–7 *The poem implies that his only friend and companion
is Tray and his sense of loss is evident when Tray
dies, 'I had always a friend in my poor dog Tray.'.*

8 *He had no money in his wallet.*

9–11 *Tray provides companionship, he provided warmth at
night and guided him as he was blind. This is shown
in the lines 'Where now shall I go, poor, forsaken,
and blind? Can I find one to guide me, so faithful and
kind?'*

12–14 *The poem begins with a contented man with a loving
relationship and a dog but when separated from
Sheelah he found himself to be poor and homeless.
He accepted his fate and didn't fight it though he felt
lonely but for his dog. After Tray died he felt even
more isolated and vulnerable.*

15 *Child's opinion on whom, after reading the poem, they feel sorrier for, the dog or man, with an explanation for their answer, e.g. I feel sorrier for the man because he is now left on his own and must try to survive.*

16 rejection
17 compilation
18 government
19 auditor
20 confession
21 unimportant
22 irresistible
23 disregard
24 immature
25 inconsistent
26 illogical
27 disown
28 impatient
29 *Jake didn't borrow a book from the library.*
30 *Gina said she wasn't playing her music too loud.*
31 *There isn't a football match this weekend./There is no football match this weekend.*
32 *There wasn't time to have dinner before going to the cinema.*
33 exhibition
34 scissors
35 solemn
36 guitar
37 mnemonic
38 cupboard
39 dumbstruck
40 whistle
41–48 'What time is it Miss Morris?' queried Kyle.
49–54 Finn screamed, 'Watch out!'
55–65 'Don't stand there, there's broken glass,' said Tracey. 'You might cut yourself.'
66 right
67 worm
68 money
69 nine
70–71 Two sentences, each starting with a fronted adverbial, e.g. *Later that morning, I heard the school had flooded.*
72 *You will be notified shortly.*
73 *A form can be obtained from the office.*
74 *Keep off the grass.*
75 *We will inform you of our decision.*
76 on
77 under
78 in
79 through
80 underneath
81 *ran*
82 *broke*
83 *ate*
84 *was*
85 *poured*
86 *were*
87 referral
88 referring
89 preferring
90 preference
91 transferred
92 transferring
93 justifiable
94 earliest
95 employment
96 ladyship
97 hungrily
98 beautiful
99 occupied
100 studious

Paper 7

1 on his own
2 because the demand for their release was too strong
3 winter
4 *because he thought Robben Island was a prison with freedoms and because it is an island it would have sea views*
5–6 *Lieutenant Van Wyck's speech cheered Nelson Mandela as it gave him strength to believe that he might leave prison relatively soon and that the cause he fought for was worthwhile and had the backing of many – otherwise release would not be considered.*
7 30 years
8 *As Nelson Mandela had many supporters it was easier for the police to move him without them knowing and under the cover of darkness. Otherwise it might stir more problems for the police to deal with.*
9 *mysteriously*
10 *noisy, energetic, excited*
11 Yes. 'the atmosphere was tense but quiet, unlike the boisterous reception I had received on my arrival on the island two years before.'
12 *He didn't intend to be treated as a boy when he was a man and in the winter it was unreasonable to expect anyone to wear shorts.*
13–15 *Despite the strength Nelson Mandela obviously found in the cause he was imprisoned for he must have felt tired, depressed and cold. The living conditions were so poor and the unknown must have been daunting. This is shown when he describes how he could walk the length of his cell in three paces, which shows how small and cramped a space he was forced to live in.*
16 reluctant
17 irrelevant
18 recipient
19 imminent
20 consistent
21 important
22 valiant
23 inefficient
24 extravagant
25 *The teacher informed Jake's mum that he had hurt himself at school today.*
26 *Lena giggled excitedly that it looked like it might snow.*
27 *Rory enquired what time the match was.*
28 *Sam informed her class that the police were investigating her missing bike.*

29–33 *Child's own passage debating the subject of recycling at his/her school. The following words need to be included: evidence, furthermore, conclusion, summary, predict, e.g. 'There is a great deal of scientific* <u>evidence</u> *that shows the benefits of recycling. I have investigated the amount of recycling done at our school and have reached the* <u>conclusion</u> *that much more can be done to recycle and help the environment.* <u>Furthermore</u>*, by recycling we are showing the community that we students care about what happens outside our school walls. In* <u>summary</u>*, I* <u>predict</u> *that if we begin to recycle cans and glass, we can reduce the amount of rubbish we put in landfills by 50 per cent.*

34 New Zealand
35 approximately
36 Heavy Goods Vehicle
37 millimetre
38 very important person
39 television
40 rest in peace
41–43 *My school backpack is so heavy because I have to carry my books, lunch box, PE kit, pencil case and ring binder.*
44–45 *My sister, who is ten years old, is acting in a pantomime this week.*
46 hate
47 faintly
48 scatter
49 litter
50 because
51 masterful
52 it
53 active
54 active
55 active
56 passive
57 active
58 active
59 passive
60 relevant
61 conscience
62 mischievous
63 beginning
64 completely
65 hindrance
66 convenience
67 unnecessary
68–72 *Clauses with a conjunction added to the main clause. Each clause must have a verb, e.g. 'The horse galloped across the field because the farmer was chasing it.'*
73 mouse
74 ox
75 dust/a bone
76 judge
77 fiddle
78–95 'What are you doing looking in my bag?' I asked.
'Is it yours?' Ben sneered. 'I was wondering what my MP3 player was doing in it.'
I stared in disbelief.

96 e n t r a n c e
97 d i c t i o n a r y
98 e n v e l o p e
99 h i s t o r y
100 d i e s e l

Paper 8

1 orange and guava juice
2 follow his daughter
3 leg
4 *because different cultures allow their children to grow up with different freedoms; obviously this school has a range of children from different cultures so Mr Patel's daughter is bound to embrace these outside the confines of home*
5–6 *insolent – behaving insultingly*
imperceptibly – very slightly, barely
7 *he felt they couldn't be trusted*
8–9 *Mma Ramotswe did not agree with Mr Patel that children should be watched. This is shown when she says, 'Although I must say I don't really like doing this. I don't like the idea of watching a child.'*
10 *He was becoming upset that his daughter would not tell him the name of the boy.*
11 *because she wanted to keep her anonymity, otherwise following her would be very hard*
12–13 *Mma Ramotswe and Mr Patel had little in common. Mma Ramotswe couldn't understand his desire to control his daughter to the extent he wanted to, she felt he hadn't caught up with modern day living and the freedoms this allowed. She also wasn't too keen on his attitudes toward women. This is shown when she says that she is a modern woman who has different ideas from him.*
14 *In his view being a detective was a man's job, not a woman's.*
15 *to show that Mma Ramotswe believes that it is important for parents to be able to let their children go*
16–27 'How long until we get to Uncle Ron's house?' groaned Simon.
'Not long now. Take a left down Tiffany Street and then we are there,' answered his dad.
They had been cycling for the last two hours and the novelty of the ride had begun to wear off. The newspaper article 'Getting Fit' had been right, maybe it would be better to do it in short manageable cycle rides!
28–34 tablecloth, database, schoolteacher, uttermost, checkout, redhead, well-being
35 *until*
36 *as*
37 *although*
38 *because*
39 *but*
40 *if*
41 atlas
42 syllabus
43 emergency
44 runway
45 speech
46 larva

47–50 *Four clauses or phrases added to improve the sentences, e.g. 'It took several minutes before they realised where they were, and what they had to do now.'*

51–57 kind, beautiful, pleasant, exquisite, attractive, friendly, delicious

58 was
59 is
60 were
61 is
62 are

63–69 'Good-bye,' called the zoo keeper. 'Don't come back next time a lion escapes!' / 'Wow!' smiled Meena. 'I didn't think we were going to get out alive.' / 'Me neither,' said Rudi. 'What was the scariest moment, Rudi?' / 'When you slipped over as the lion started running towards us!' giggled Rudi. / 'Mine too!' / 'Let's go home and tell your Mum.' / 'She'll never believe us!'

70–75 *The completion of six metaphors – an expression in which something is described in terms usually associated with another, e.g. 'The clouds were cotton balls.'*

76 *fought*
77 *bough*
78 *tough*
79 *thought*
80 *dough*
81 *borough*
82–83 *cough through*
84–86 to, two, to
87–88 too, to
89–90 to, two
91–93 too, two, to
94 *pre*
95 *mis*
96 *con*
97 *re/dis*
98 *ex/re*
99 *co*
100 *ab*

Paper 9

1 to raise funds for leukaemia research
2 Michael/David/Tam
3 its theme park
4 *With her family arriving she felt she had finished her journey and Dan was the only one missing and she wanted him to be part of it.*
5 *when everything freezes; when you are aware of everything around you*
6 *Time stood still for Sally because seeing her family again at the end of her walk was a time of great happiness and emotion.*
7 *She felt elated and carefree as she set out on the final day of walking with her family around her – nothing worried her. She now knew for sure she would achieve her goal.*
8–9 lull (line 17) and scrutinising (line 34)

10–12 *Evidence supporting how Sally felt on completing her walk: happy, content, overwhelmed, tired, excited, etc. 'Sally felt excited and happy for completing her walk. This is shown when she says that everyone looked wonderful and that it was an extraordinary day.'*

13–15 *Characteristics of Sally's personality that helped her achieve her goal, e.g. brave, determined, strong. Child needs to give reasons, e.g. 'Sally is a brave and caring person. She is brave because she undertook a difficult challenge that lasted many months and which she did on her own. She is caring because she did the walk to raise money for leukaemia research even though her son had died.'*

16 to advertise
17 to depart
18 to fly
19 to applaud
20 to conclude
21 the girls' hats
22 the churches' spires
23 Lilia's home
24 James's computer
25 his friend's bike
26 the teacher's scissors

27–38 *Three sentences using the words provided, plus two verbs and two adjectives, e.g. The young girl ran quickly towards the frightened horse who was galloping across the field.*

39 *without furniture*
40 *in low spirits*
41 *polite*
42 *a person who watches*
43 *helped*
44 *to try*
45 *to look like*
46 practice
47 practise
48 principal
49 principle
50 their
51 there
52 course
53 coarse
54 omelette
55 minnow
56 shallow
57 flannel
58 arrive
59 quarrel
60 goggle
61 struggle
62 It's snowing; I'm so excited.

63–66 People enjoy summer for a number of reasons: it's warm; they enjoy doing things outside; they can eat BBQs; it stays light late into the evening.

67 We have two types of tree in our garden: beech and oak.
68 lump of lead – head
69 skin and blister – sister
70 frog and toad – road
71 mince pies – eyes

72 sugar and honey – money
73 dog and bone – telephone
74 Barnet Fair – hair
75 *shall, might, will, may*
76 *will, might*
77 *won't, shan't*
78 *would, should*
79 *will, might*
80 annually
81 frequently
82 regretted
83 decided
84 audience
85 congregation
86 Occasionally
87 cleverest
88 poorest
89 worst
90 ugliest
91 reddest
92 most generous
93 best
94 most curious
95–100 owlet, duckling, piglet, lambkin, statuette, eaglet

Paper 10

1 cleaning the silver
2 bullets
3–6 *The story is about a town that is bombed during a war. This is shown by the all-clear siren, the bullet damage, and the fact that a town was bombed.*
7 *because she was shocked by the damage done to the room*
8 *'knives and forks like a shoal of shining fish.'*
9 *dotted, lined with small holes*
10 *She reacted in this way because she was probably dazed, confused and worried about what had happened.*
11 *'Then she realised that whatever had done it had passed straight through the spot where she had been standing cleaning the silver.'*
12 *'Staring at the tea-roses peeping over Mr Marshall's fence, the same as they did every year.'*
13–15 *At first she is confused about what has happened and focuses entirely on her immediate surroundings. She then becomes worried about the safety of others, as is shown when she runs outside to check on the milkman. The enormity of what has happened hits her making her feel weary and yet only when someone shows concern for her does she feel her emotions might take hold, as when she says she nearly wept, but she keeps herself in check.*
16 sign
17 hope
18 state
19 doubt

20 decorate
21 lazy
22 instant
23 extend
24–25 I'm sorry we're going to be late.
26 Liz fed Aimee's ducks.
27 Where's the party?
28 The dogs' coats were muddy and wet.
29–31 Let's hide Jake's homework here, he'll never find it.
32 *between*
33 *behind*
34 *on*
35 *into*
36 *in*
37 *between*
38 *into*
39 baroness
40 niece
41 nanny-goat
42 duck
43 duchess
44 doe or hind
45–48 *An adjectival phrase, a group of words describing a noun, for each of the given subjects, e.g. a shiny, black horse*
49 autumn
50 kitchen
51 handkerchief
52 subtlety
53 psalm
54 science
55 wrench
56 column
57 insistent
58 insinuate
59 insincere
60 inseparable
61 insensitive
62 inscription
63–89 'Who is there?' cried Steven, putting his head out of his bedroom window.
'It's Mike, Steven.'
'What do you want?' he asked.
'Sadie has fallen from the swings. Can you ask your dad to come as quickly as possible, she needs a doctor to check her leg.'
90–91 Every afternoon, as they were coming home from school, Mina and Toby used to play by the banks of the river.
92 It was a lovely large garden, with soft green grass.
93–94 High above the city, on a tall column, stood the statue of Nelson.
95–96 *off-centre, off-line*
97–98 *over-sensitive, over-cooked*
99–100 *re-cover, re-elect*

Write one word instead of the words in bold.

D 1

45 We **kept out of the way of** Mum because she was cross. _____

46 Mr Martin says that my work is **getting much better**. _____

47 In case we forgot, we said the message **over and over again**. _____

48 The fraction had to be **turned upside down**. _____

49 **A short time ago** we went to the circus. _____

50 The boy was told to **come back** tomorrow. _____

51 The cyclist knocked over a **person who was walking**. _____

7

Rewrite the following passage, adding the missing capital letters.

D 5

52–61 as zoe and rupa slept soundly strange things began to happen. a night to remember, the book rupa had been reading, suddenly fell open at a page. the page told the story of a ghost which haunted the streets of skegness every thursday night.

_____

_____

_____

_____

10

Add two more words that are based on the following **root words**.

D 11

Example: help   *helping*   *helpful*

62–63 love   _____   _____

64–65 clear   _____   _____

66–67 cycle   _____   _____

68–69 pay   _____   _____

8

Complete these words with *cial* or *tial*.

E 1

70 offi_____   **71** finan_____

72 spe_____   **73** par_____

74 confiden_____   **75** commer_____

76 essen_____

7

Underline separately the **clauses** in each sentence.

77–78 Wes thought that he must have been dreaming.

79–80 My Dad collapsed into his chair because the run had exhausted him!

81–82 The picture fell from the wall, glass smashing everywhere.

83–84 Judy wondered whether the book might be useful for her project.

These **phrases** are often used in formal letters or documents. What do they mean?

85 further to your recent correspondence

_____

86 forms may be obtained from

_____

87 those wishing to attend

_____

88 notice is hereby served

_____

Draw a line (/) every time a new line should have been started in the following dialogue.

89–94 'Where is Jess,' moaned Dad./'We really need to get going or we will miss our ferry.'/'She is coming, I can hear her racing down the stairs,' replied Mum./'About time too!' continued Dad./As Jess climbed into the car, Mum enquired, 'Have you got your coat?'/'Oops ... shall I go and get it?' Jess asked./'Yes and be VERY quick,' Dad almost shouted, 'I'm losing my patience!'/'Sorry,' she called as she flew into the house.

Write the number (1, 2 or 3) next to each word it has derived from:

(1)   another language

(2)   names of places or people

(3)   imitating sounds

95 sizzle   _____   **96** wellington   _____

97 spaghetti   _____   **98** splutter   _____

99 photograph   _____   **100** hoover   _____

Now go to the Progress Chart to record your score!   Total   100

D 2

8

D 2

4

D 3

D 12

6

6

B

Poor Dog Tray

On the green banks of Shannon when Sheelah was nigh,
No blithe Irish lad was so happy as I;
No harp like my own could so cheerily play,
And wherever I went was my poor dog Tray.

When at last I was forced from my Sheelah to part, 5
She said (while the sorrow was big at her heart),
Oh! remember your Sheelah when far, far away:
And be kind, my dear Pat, to our poor dog Tray.

Poor dog! he was faithful and kind to be sure,
And he constantly loved me although I was poor; 10
When the sour-looking folk sent me heartless away,
I had always a friend in my poor dog Tray.

When the road was so dark, and the night was so cold,
And Pat and his dog were grown weary and old,
How snugly we slept in my old coat of grey, 15
And he lick'd me for kindness – my old dog Tray.

Though my wallet was scant I remember'd his case,
Nor refused my last crust to his pitiful face;
But he died at my feet on a cold winter day,
And I play'd a sad lament for my poor dog Tray. 20

Where now shall I go, poor, forsaken, and blind?
Can I find one to guide me, so faithful and kind?
To my sweet native village, so far, far away,
I can never more return with my poor dog Tray.

Thomas Campbell

Underline the correct answers.

1 In which country is this poem set?

(England, Ireland, Wales)

2 What is the gentleman's name?

(Sheelah, Tray, Pat)

3 At what time of year did Tray die?

(winter, summer, autumn)

3

Answer these questions.

4–5 Write two possible reasons why the man had to leave Sheelah.

_____

_____

6–7 Use evidence from the poem to explain how we know the man was lonely.

_____

_____

8 What is meant by 'Though my wallet was scant …' (line 17)?

_____

9–11 Give two reasons why the dog Tray is so important to the man. Use evidence from the passage to support your answer.

_____

_____

_____

12–14 Describe the personal journey this man makes through the poem. How does his self-worth change?

_____

_____

_____

15 Who in this poem do you feel more sorry for, the dog or the man? Why?

_____

12

D 6

Form **nouns** from the **verbs** in bold to fill each gap.

16 reject Bola had a sense of _____ as his dog ran off to meet his sister.

17 compile Brian put together a _____ of his favourite music.

18 govern The _____ insisted seat belts should be worn.

19 audit The _____ checked through the files thoroughly.

20 confess The burglar gave a detailed _____.

5

34

Write an **antonym** for each of these words by adding a **prefix**.

21 important _____   22 resistible _____

23 regard _____   24 mature _____

25 consistent _____   26 logical _____

27 own _____   28 patient _____

Rewrite these sentences without double negatives.

29 Jake didn't borrow no book from the library.

_____

30 Gina said she wasn't playing no music too loud.

_____

31 There isn't no football match this weekend.

_____

32 There wasn't no time to have dinner before going to the cinema.

_____

Rewrite each word, adding the missing silent letter so that each word is spelt correctly.

33 exibition _____   34 sissors _____

35 solem _____   36 gitar _____

37 nemonic _____   38 cuboard _____

39 dumstruck _____   40 whisle _____

Punctuate these sentences correctly.

41–48 what time is it miss morris queried kyle

_____

49–54 finn screamed watch out

_____

55–65 don't stand there there's broken glass said tracey you might cut yourself

_____

Complete the following proverbs.

66 Two wrongs don't make a _____.

67 The early bird catches the _____.

68 A fool and his _____ are soon parted.

69 A stitch in time saves _____.

Write two sentences that begin with a **fronted adverbial**.

70 _____

71 _____

Using official-type language, rewrite each of these sentences.

72 We will let you know soon.

_____

73 You can get a form from the office.

_____

74 Please don't walk on the grass.

_____

75 We will let you know what we decide.

_____

Underline the **prepositions** in the following sentences.

76 Ahmed slipped on the banana skin.

77 The hedgehog slept under the autumn leaves.

78 The test papers were hidden in amongst the workbooks.

79 The ball went through the goalie's legs!

80 Sam hid underneath his bed.

4

2

D 1

4

D 6

5

Complete each of these sentences in the **past tense**.

81 I _____ to school because I was late.

82 When I jumped off the wall I _____ my leg.

83 George _____ his lunch quickly.

84 Tess _____ late for the party.

85 It _____ with rain all day.

86 The children _____ playing on the climbing equipment.

⬤ 6

Complete these word sums.

87 refer + al = _____

88 refer + ing = _____

89 prefer + ing = _____

90 prefer + ence = _____

91 transfer + ed = _____

92 transfer + ing = _____

⬤ 6

Add the **suffixes** to these words ending in y. Don't forget any necessary spelling changes.

93 justify + able _____

94 early + est _____

95 employ + ment _____

96 lady + ship _____

97 hungry + ly _____

98 beauty + ful _____

99 occupy + ed _____

100 study + ous _____

⬤ 8

Now go to the Progress Chart to record your score!   Total ⬤ 100

Paper 7

Nelson Mandela was sentenced to life imprisonment and started his prison years in the notorious Robben Island Prison.

At midnight, I was awake and staring at the ceiling – images from the trial were still rattling around in my head – when I heard steps coming down the hallway. I was locked in my own cell, away from the others. There was a knock at my door and I could see Colonel Aucamp's face at the bars. 'Mandela,' he said in a husky whisper, 'are you awake?' 5

I told him I was. 'You are a lucky man,' he said. 'We are taking you to a place where you will have your freedom. You will be able to move around; you'll see the ocean and the sky, not just grey walls.'

He intended no sarcasm, but I well knew that the place he was referring to would not afford me the freedom I longed for. He then remarked rather cryptically, 'As long 10 as you don't make trouble, you'll get everything you want.'

Aucamp then woke the others, all of whom were in a single cell, ordering them to pack their things. Fifteen minutes later we were making our way through the iron labyrinth of Pretoria Local, with its endless series of clanging metal doors echoing in our ears. 15

Once outside, the seven of us – Walter, Raymond, Govan, Kathy, Andrew, Elias and myself – were handcuffed and piled into the back of a police van ... The warders provided us with sandwiches and cold drinks and Lieutenant Van Wyck was perched in the back with us. He was a pleasant fellow, and during a lull in the singing, he offered his unsolicited opinion on our future. 'Well,' he said, 'you chaps won't 20 be in prison long. The demand for your release is too strong. In a year or two, you will get out and you will return as national heroes. Crowds will cheer you, everyone will want to be your friend, women will want you. Ag, you fellows have it made.' We listened without comment, but I confess his speech cheered me considerably. Unfortunately, his prediction turned out to be off by nearly three decades. 25

We were departing quietly, secretly, under a heavy police escort, in the middle of the night, and in less than half an hour we found ourselves at a small military airport outside the city ...

From here Nelson was put on a plane to Robben Island.

... We landed on a military airstrip on one end of the island. It was a grim, overcast 30 day ... the cold winter wind whipped through our thin prison uniforms. We were met by guards with automatic weapons; the atmosphere was tense but quiet, unlike the boisterous reception I had received on my arrival on the island two years before.

We were driven to the old jail, an isolated stone building, where we were ordered to strip while standing outside. One of the ritual indignities of prison life is that 35 when you are transferred from one prison to another, the first thing that happens is that you change from the garb of the old prison to that of the new. When we were undressed, we were thrown the plain khaki uniforms of Robben Island.

Apartheid's regulations extended even to clothing. All of us, except Kathy, received short trousers, an insubstantial jersey, and a canvas jacket. Kathy, the one Indian   *40* among us, was given long trousers ... Short trousers for Africans were meant to remind us that we were 'boys'. I put on the short trousers that day, but I vowed that I would not put up with them for long.

I was assigned a cell at the head of the corridor. It overlooked the courtyard and had a small eye-level window. I could walk the length of my cell in three paces.   *45* When I lay down, I could feel the wall with my feet and my head grazed the concrete at the other side. The width was about six feet, and the walls were at least two feet thick. Each cell had a white card posted outside of it with our name and our prison service number. Mine read, 'N Mandela 466/64,' which meant I was the 466th prisoner admitted to the island in 1964. I was forty-six years old, a political   *50* prisoner with a life sentence, and that small cramped space was to be my home for I knew not how long.

From Long Walk to Freedom: The Autobiography of Nelson Mandela

Underline the correct answers.

1 After the trial was Nelson Mandela in a cell on his own or with others?

(on his own, with others, the passage doesn't state)

2 Why did Lieutenant Van Wyck believe Nelson Mandela and his friends would soon be released?

(because they had served their sentence, because the demand for their release was too strong, because there wasn't room in the prison to detain them)

3 In which season did Nelson Mandela arrive at Robben Island?

(winter, spring, autumn)

3

Answer these questions.

4 Colonel Aucamp told Nelson Mandela he was a 'lucky' man (line 6). Why did he think Nelson Mandela was lucky?

_____

5–6 Give two reasons why you think Lieutenant Van Wyck's speech cheered Nelson Mandela.

_____

_____

7 For approximately how many years was Nelson Mandela in prison?

_____

8 Why do you think Nelson Mandela and his friends were 'departing quietly, secretly, under a heavy police escort, in the middle of the night' (line 26)?

_____

9 What does the word 'cryptically' mean (line 10)?

_____

10 What does the word 'boisterous' mean (line 33)?

_____

11 Had Nelson Mandela previously been to Robben Island? Copy the line from the passage that answers this question.

_____

12 Why do you think Nelson Mandela vowed that he would not put up with short trousers for long?

_____

_____

13–15 Read the final paragraph of this passage again. How do you think Nelson Mandela felt at this time? Use evidence from the passage to support your answer.

_____

_____

_____

_____

12

E 1

Complete each of these to make a word ending in *ant* or *ent*.

16 reluct_____   **17** irrelev_____   **18** recipi_____

19 immin_____   **20** consist_____   **21** import_____

22 vali_____   **23** ineffici_____   **24** extravag_____

9

D 12

Write these sentences as **reported speech**.

25 'Jake hurt himself at school today,' the teacher informed his mum.

_____

26 'It looks like it might snow,' giggled Lena excitedly.

_____

27 'What time is the match?' Rory enquired.

_____

28 'The police are investigating my missing bike,' Sam informed her class.

, _____

Use each of these words in a short passage debating whether your school should recycle more than just paper.

     evidence   furthermore   conclusion   summary   predict

29–33

_____

_____

_____

_____

_____

Write the following **abbreviations** in full.

34 NZ   _____

35 approx   _____

36 HGV   _____

37 mm   _____

38 VIP   _____

39 TV   _____

40 RIP   _____

Write two sentences, one with three commas separating words in a list and the other with two commas used as a slight pause or break between parts in a sentence.

41–43 _____

_____

_____

44–45 _____

_____

Match each word with its correct word class.

litter   hate   it   masterful   scatter   faintly   because

46 abstract noun _____

47 adverb _____

48 verb _____

49 collective noun _____

50 conjunction _____

51 adjective _____

52 pronoun _____

State whether each of these sentences has an **active** or **passive** verb.

53 The wind blew Mr Tomkin's hat off.   _____

54 Tuhil caught a huge fish.   _____

55 The rain soaked the children walking home from school.   _____

56 Hannah was hurt as she slipped on the wet rocks.   _____

57 Jacob jumped off the climbing frame.   _____

58 Water spurted from the burst pipe.   _____

59 Caroline was scared of the dark.   _____

The words below are spelt incorrectly. Rewrite them correctly.

60 relevent   _____   **61** consciance   _____

62 mischevous   _____   **63** begining   _____

64 completly   _____   **65** hindrence   _____

66 conveniance   _____   **67** unnecesary   _____

Add a **clause** with a **conjunction** to each of these main clauses.

D 2

68 The horse galloped across the field _____

_____

69 The waiter tripped holding two plates of food _____

_____

70 The baby slept peacefully _____

_____

71 Poppy finally finished her book _____

_____

72 At last the audience were seated _____

_____

5

Complete the following **similes**.

C 4

73 As quiet as a _____.

74 As strong as an _____.

75 As dry as _____.

76 As sober as a _____.

77 As fit as a _____.

5

Rewrite this passage correctly.

D 5

78–95 what are you doing looking in my bag i asked

is it yours ben sneered i was wondering what my MP3 player was doing in it

i stared in disbelief

_____

_____

_____

_____

_____

18

Underline the unstressed vowel sound in each word.

96 e n t r a n c e

97 d i c t i o n a r y

98 e n v e l o p e

99 h i s t o r y

100 d i e s e l

Now go to the Progress Chart to record your score! Total 100

Paper 8

Mma Ramotswe runs the No. 1 Ladies' Detective Agency in Africa. She is the only female private detective in Botswana.

As Mr Patel spoke, the door to his study, which had been closed behind them when they had entered, opened and a woman came into the room. She was a local woman and she greeted Mma Ramotswe politely in Setswana before offering her a tray on which various glasses of fruit juice were set. Mma Ramotswe chose a glass of guava juice and thanked the servant. Mr Patel helped himself to orange juice and   5
then impatiently waved the servant out of the room with his stick, waiting until she had gone before he continued to speak.

'I have spoken to her about this,' he said. 'I have made it very clear to her. I told her that I don't care what other children are doing – that is their parents' business, not mine. I have made it very clear that she is not to go about the town with boys or   10
see boys after school. That is final.'

He tapped his artificial leg lightly with his walking stick and then looked at Mma Ramotswe expectantly.

Mma Ramotswe cleared her throat. 'You want me to do something about this?' she said quietly. 'Is this why you have asked me here this evening?'   15

Mr Patel nodded. 'That is precisely why. I want you to find out who this boy is, and then I will speak to him.'

Mma Ramotswe stared at Mr Patel. Had he the remotest idea, she wondered, how young people behaved these days, especially at a school like Maru-a-Pula, where there were all those foreign children, even children from the American   20
Embassy and such places? She had heard about Indian fathers trying to arrange marriages, but she had never actually encountered such behaviour. And here was Mr Patel assuming that she would agree with him; that she would take exactly the same view.

'Wouldn't it be better to speak to her?' she asked gently. 'If you asked her who   25
the young man was, then she might tell you.'

Mr Patel reached for his stick and tapped his tin leg.

'Not at all,' he said sharply, his voice becoming shrill. 'Notat all. I have already been asking her for three weeks, maybe four weeks. And she gives no answer. She is dumb insolent.' ...   30

... She looked up. Mr Patel was watching her with his dark eyes, the tip of his walking stick tapping almost imperceptibly on the floor.

'I'll find out for you.' she said. 'Although I must say I don't really like doing this. I don't like the idea of watching a child.'

'But children must be watched!' expostulated Mr Patel. 'If parents don't watch their children, then what happens? You answer that!' 35

'There comes a time when they must have their own lives,' said Mma Ramotswe. 'We have to let go.'

'Nonsense!' shouted Mr Patel. 'Modern nonsense. My father beat me when I was twenty-two! Yes, he beat me for making a mistake in the shop. And I deserved it. 40 None of this modern nonsense.'

Mma Ramotswe rose to her feet.

'I am a modern lady,' she said. 'So perhaps we have different ideas. But that has nothing to do with it. I have agreed to do as you have asked me. Now all that you need to do is to let me see a photograph of this girl, so that I can know who it is I 45 am going to be watching.'

Mr Patel struggled to his feet, straightening the tin leg with his hands as he did so.

'No need for a photograph,' he said. 'I can produce the girl herself. You can look at her.'

Mma Ramotswe raised her hands in protest. 'But then she will know me,' she 50 said. 'I must be able to be unobserved.'

'Ah!' said Mr Patel. 'A very good idea. You detectives are very clever men.'

'Women,' said Mma Ramotswe.

Mr Patel looked at her sideways, but said nothing. He had no time for modern ideas.

As she left the house, Mma Ramotswe thought: He has four children; I have 55 none. He is not a good father this man, because he loves his children too much – he wants to own them. You have to let go. You have to let go.

Extract from *The No. 1 Ladies' Detective Agency* by Alexander McCall Smith

Underline the correct answers.

1 What drinks do we know were on offer to Mma Ramotswe?

(orange juice only, guava juice only, orange and guava juice)

2 What was Mr Patel asking Mma Ramotswe to do?

(follow his son, follow his daughter, follow a group of children)

3 Mr Patel had an artificial body part. Which part was it?

(leg, arm, hand)

3

Answer these questions.

4 Why would Mma Ramotswe think that foreign children at Mr Patel's daughter's school would make a difference to her behaviour?

_____

5–6 What is the meaning of the words 'insolent' (line 30) and 'imperceptibly' (line 32)?

_____

_____

7 Why do you think Mr Patel felt that '... children must be watched!' (line 35)?

_____

8–9 Explain whether Mma Ramotswe agreed with Mr Patel about children needing to be watched. Use evidence from the passage to support your answer.

_____

_____

10 Why did Mr Patel's voice become 'shrill' (line 28)?

_____

11 Why didn't Mma Ramotswe want to meet Mr Patel's daughter?

_____

12–13 Using evidence from the passage, discuss Mma Ramotswe's feelings towards Mr Patel.

_____

_____

14 Why did Mr Patel say 'You detectives are very clever men' to Mma Ramotswe?

_____

15 Look again at the last paragraph. Why does the author repeat the last line?

_____

12

D 5

Circle the letters in the passage that should be capitals.

16–27 'how long until we get to uncle ron's house?' groaned simon.

'not long now. take a left down tiffany street and then we are there,' answered his dad.

they had been cycling for the last two hours and the novelty of the ride had begun to wear off. the newspaper article 'getting fit' had been right, maybe it would be better to do it in short manageable cycle rides!

12

Using a word from each column write seven **compound words**.

D 11

28–34 table   out

     data   teacher

     school   being

     utter   cloth

     check   most

     red   base

     well   head

_____   _____   _____

_____   _____   _____

_____

7

Add a different **conjunction** to each sentence.

D 6

35 The stars glistened in the sky _____ the clouds hid them from view.

36 Excitement welled up inside Hannah _____ she got closer to the Queen.

37 Rolf ate his sandwiches _____ it was still too early for lunch.

38 Fran was cross with herself _____ she forgot her swimming costume.

39 Since Rashid broke his leg he still couldn't run _____ he could walk.

40 Mum wondered _____ her washing would dry.

6

Write the **singular** form of these words.

E 2

41 atlases   _____   42 syllabi   _____

43 emergencies   _____   44 runways   _____

45 speeches   _____   46 larvae   _____

6

Add a **clause** or **phrase** to each sentence.

D 2

47 It took several minutes before they realised where they were.

_____

_____

48 The thought of it terrified the giant.

_____

_____

49 The bird crashed into the closed window.

_____

_____

50 The teacher's explanation confused Kelly even more!

_____

_____

Write seven **synonyms** for the word _nice_.

51–57 _____   _____   _____

_____   _____   _____

_____

Underline the correct **verb** form in each sentence.

58 There (was/were) time to get home before our friends arrived.

59 Marianne (is/are) comfortable in her bed.

60 The dogs (was/were) chasing after the rabbit.

61 There (is/are) a knock at the door.

62 Tim and Sally (is/are) best friends.

Draw a line (/) every time a new line should have been started in the following dialogue.

63–69 'Good-bye,' called the zoo keeper. 'Don't come back next time a lion escapes!' 'Wow!' smiled Meena. 'I didn't think we were going to get out alive.' 'Me neither,' said Rudi. 'What was the scariest moment, Rudi?' 'When you slipped over as the lion started running towards us!' giggled Rudi. 'Mine too!' 'Let's go home and tell your Mum.' 'She'll never believe us!'

Write each word in a **metaphor**.

70 clouds   _____

71 snow   _____

4

D 9

7

D 6

5

D 3

D 12

7

C 4

72 waterfall _____

73 bull _____

74 dew _____

75 quilt _____ ◯ 6

D 5

Write a word that has the same pronunciation as each of these words.

76 brought _____ **77** plough _____

78 rough _____ **79** nought _____

80 though _____ **81** thorough _____

Write two more *ough* words that have a different pronunciation to all of the ough words in 76–81.

82–83 c_____ th_____ ◯ 8

E 1

Write in each gap *to*, *too* or *two*.

84–86 It is time _____ take the _____ dogs for a walk

_____ the park.

87–88 He's not _____ well today so I'm taking him _____ the doctor's.

89–90 I think we should start _____ cook the _____ fish on the BBQ.

91–93 I've eaten _____ much, I'll have to undo _____ trouser

buttons _____ feel comfortable! ◯ 10

E 2

Add a different **prefix** to each of these words.

94 _____caution **95** _____construe

96 _____front **97** _____connect

98 _____patriate **99** _____education

100 _____normal ◯ 7

Now go to the Progress Chart to record your score! Total ◯ 100

49

Paper 9

Sally Thomas walked from Land's End (the south-west tip of England) to John O'Groats (the most northern point of mainland Scotland). Sally's son was suffering from leukaemia and while in hospital with him she spotted a photograph pinned up on a noticeboard.

'Well done Finlay!' read the caption beneath the picture of an ex-leukaemia patient who had ridden an ancient bike from Land's End to John O'Groats, thereby raising several thousand pounds for leukaemia research. I decided there and then that I too would make this journey, though on foot rather than bicycle. I decided that I would do it whatever the outcome of Jim's illness; if he survived, it would be a thanksgiving, 5 and if not, funds raised would contribute towards research aimed at eliminating this cruel and devastating disease.

Sally started her walk on the first anniversary of Jim's death. It took her three and a half months to complete. Her family joined her for the last day.

Keiss to John O'Groats 10

Last night all that was missing was little Dan, though I did talk to him on the phone. I was so excited when they all arrived that I kept thinking I'd finished the journey, and so one of my first thoughts was, 'I must ring Dan!'

It was wonderful to see them all. I'd seen the car coming over the horizon from my bedroom window and so was waiting by the side of the road when they arrived. 15 And then there was a peculiar moment when nothing seemed to happen. There was a lull, and I thought, 'Why don't they get out of the car?' It can only have been for a split second, but it seemed to last forever. I suppose it was a distortion of time such as you hear people describe when they're about to experience a car crash or similar – moments of danger or high emotion, when 'time stood still.' I've never experienced it before. But they got out eventually, beaming and smiling, and then we were all kissing and hugging each other in the quiet, dusty road outside the Sinclair Bay Hotel, and I shall never forget it. They thought I looked thin and I thought they looked wonderful! We had a lovely meal together, everybody talking at the same time, and I've no notion of what we ate.   *20*   *25*

And how lovely to set out all together this morning, me without a care in the world! (Still carrying my pack though, emptied of some of its contents. I wouldn't let them carry it for me on the last day!) Michael, David and Tam accompanied me all the way and Berwyn did a bit of sightseeing in Wick and then parked the car in John O'Groats and walked back out to meet us. It was so good to be walking with them on what I still couldn't quite believe was the last day. It seemed quite normal, though I did feel a bit light-headed and couldn't concentrate at all. It was a main road all the way of course but there was hardly any traffic, and we fair skipped along, scrutinising the horizon for our first sight of the sea *ahead*.   *30*

At last there it was, the sea in front of us, and the first of many signs saying JOHN O'GROATS. We took lots of pictures, draping ourselves around the signs, and walked the last few hundred yards to The End. It's far nicer here than in Land's End with its theme park and commercial tat. John O'Groats is just a big hotel, the sea, and a few small souvenir shops selling lots of postcards ... we all milled around talking and laughing in friendly and slightly embarrassed fashion on this unique, never-to-be-repeated occasion. What an extraordinary day! And how happy I am to be going home tomorrow!   *35*   *40*

Extract from *A Walk for Jim* by Sally Thomas

Underline the correct answers.

1 Why did Sally walk from Land's End to John O'Groats?

(to visit her son, to raise funds for leukaemia research, to get fit)

2 Who completed the final day's walking with Sally?

(Berwyn/David/Tam, Michael/Dan/Tam, Michael/David/Tam)

3 What did Sally not like about Land's End?

(its rocky seaside, its theme park, its lack of shops)   3

Answer these questions.

4 Why did Sally think she '... must ring Dan!' (line 13)?

_____

5 Describe in your own words what is meant by 'when time stood still' (line 20).

_____

6 Why did time stand still for Sally?

_____

7 Why did Sally set out 'without a care in the world'?

_____

8–9 Write down the words from the passage that mean:

A temporary period of inactivity.   _____

Looking at carefully.   _____

10–12 Using evidence from the passage describe how Sally felt on completing her journey.

_____

_____

_____

13–15 How would you describe the sort of person Sally is? Give reasons for your answer.

_____

_____

_____

12

D 6

Change each of the **nouns** in bold to the infinitive of the **verb**.

Example: He was good at **multiplication**.   _to multiply_

16 She saw the **advertisement** on television.   _____

17 The **departure** of the train was delayed.   _____

18 The '**_Flight_** of the Bumble Bee' is a popular piece of music.   _____

19 The **applause** lasted for several minutes.   _____

20 The story reached an interesting **conclusion**.   _____

5

Write these in the possessive case, i.e. with an apostrophe.

D 5

Example: the bone of the dog   *the dog's bone*

21 the hats of the girls   _____

22 the spires of the churches   _____

23 the home of Lilia   _____

24 the computer of James   _____

25 the bike of his friend   _____

26 the scissors of the teacher   _____

6

Using the words provided, plus two **verbs** and two **adjectives** of your own, make three sentences.

D 6

27–30 The   girl   towards   the   horse

_____

_____

31–34 The   kite   in   the   sky

_____

_____

35–38 Monty   the   dog   on   the   man

_____

_____

12

Write a **definition** for each of these words.

39 unfurnished   _____

40 dejected   _____

41 courteous   _____

42 spectator   _____

43 assisted   _____

44 endeavour   _____

45 resemble   _____

7

Underline the correct **homophone**.

advice – noun
advise – verb

E 2

46 The doctor's (practise, <u>practice</u>) is in Warwick Road.

47 They (<u>practise</u>, practice) their judo.

48 The (<u>principal</u>, principle) of the college had taught abroad.

49 It was a matter of (principal, <u>principle</u>) that he should write the letter.

50 Where is (their, there) rabbit?

51 I put it over (their, there).

52 The (coarse, course) of the river meanders through the field.

53 The material she used was very (coarse, course).

8

Add the correct double letters to create a word.

E 2

rr   ll   tt   nn   gg

54 omle _____ e

55 mi _____ ow

56 sha _____ ow

57 fla _____ el

58 a _____ ive

59 qua _____ el

60 go _____ le

61 stru _____

Add the missing colons and semicolons to these sentences.

D 1

62 It's snowing I'm so excited.

63–66 People enjoy summer for a number of reasons it's warm they enjoy doing things outside they can eat BBQs it stays light late into the evening.

67 We have two types of tree in our garden beech and oak.

6

Match, with a line, the Cockney rhyming slang with its meaning.

68 lump of lead   hair

69 skin and blister   telephone

70 frog and toad   head

71 mince pies   money

72 sugar and honey   road

73 dog and bone   eyes

74 Barnet Fair   sister

7

Add a suitable helper **verb** to each of these **conditional** sentences (when one thing depends on something else).

D 6

75 I _____ ring when I get home if my mum lets me.

76 Should it rain, we _____ buy an umbrella.

77 I _____ do anything unless I hear from you.

78 I _____ like to go swimming, providing it doesn't rain.

79 Your purse _____ be stolen if you leave the car unlocked.

5

Write a **synonym** for the words in bold.

D 9

80 They went on holiday **each year**. _____

81 Sue goes there quite **often**. _____

82 She **was sorry** that she had been naughty. _____

83 Tom **made up his mind** to go to the cinema. _____

84 The **people who had been watching** clapped loudly when the play ended. _____

85 The **people at the church service** listened attentively to the vicar's sermon. _____

86 **Now and then** we go to the cinema. _____

7

Write the **superlative** form of the **adjective** on the left.

87 **clever**   That is the _____ answer of all.

88 **poor**   The _____ families live there.

89 **bad**   They reported the _____ gale for ten years.

90 **ugly**   She was the _____ of the sisters.

91 **red**   My apple is the _____ one I have ever seen.

92 **generous**   Mum is the _____ person I know.

93 **good**   That is the _____ conker I have played with.

94 **curious**   Alice thought it was the _____ thing she'd seen.

8

Underline the **diminutives**.

95–100   model   bull   owlet   fireplace   lioness

         duckling   hare   gander   piglet   dog

         lambkin   magazine   statuette   eaglet

6

She picked herself up, and stared about her. Somebody had chopped a long hole in the cellar ceiling; ragged ends of lath and plaster hung, lit by light trickling down from the dining room above.

Bemused, she heard the siren sound the long, unbroken note of the all-clear. She wished they would make their minds up. She climbed the stairs feeling very weary; the cat kept on rubbing against her, as if wanting to be petted. It nearly tripped her up; she yelled at it angrily.

She forced back the dining-room door, which seemed to have swung to. And stood unable to move.

The windows were gone; the curtains were blowing out through the jagged edges, tangling and tearing themselves. But, more amazingly, the dining-room table lay tilted together in two halves; somebody had chopped it in two. All the silver she had been cleaning lay in the valley in the middle, knives and forks like a shoal of shining fish. On top lay a battered chunk of metal, torn into a kind of silver lace. She had to pick it up before she recognised her coffee-pot. She only recognised it by the handle ... There was a long hole in her carpet, with the darkness showing underneath. The musty smell in the cellar came up to her, with the acrid smell of spilt 'Silvo'. The wall was covered with great pale stars where the plaster had burst out through dangling strips of her best striped Regency wallpaper ...

What had done it?

Then she realised that whatever had done it had passed straight through the spot where she had been standing cleaning the silver. But for the cat ...

Where *was* the cat? Was it hurt?

But it came walking sedately out of the hall, sniffed the wreckage carefully, then sat down and began to wash its shoulder. 25

She remembered the milkman. She ran outside. There was the same long deep kind of hole running across the lawn from a narrow gap in the privet hedge. There were little silver mushrooms scattered all over the lawn. She absently bent and picked one up. It was very heavy for its size. She put it in the pocket of her pinafore. She only realised later that it was a machine-gun bullet, flattened from hitting the 30 brickwork of the bay window.

The milkman was not where he had fallen. He was further up the road, bending over his horse, among a little crowd of people who were gathering. She could see the horse's head and neck, sticking out, through their legs. The head was moving, trying to lift itself ... 35

Slowly, she walked up to the little crowd. She was terrified of what she would see, so she kept her head down. The surface of the road was pitted with a long line of little holes that led straight as an arrow to her fence, her garden, her dining room. Dozens of the little silver mushrooms ...

She reached the back of the crowd; saw their legs. Heard the milkman sobbing, 40 saying things between sobs.

'She's the best horse I ever had. She knew her own way back to the stable. Oh, God, fetch a vet somebody. I can't bear watching her suffer ...'

Mrs Smiley just stood, feeling weary beyond belief. Back turned to the crowd and the terrible breathing of the dying horse. Staring at the tea-roses peeping over 45 Mr Marshall's fence, the same as they did every year.

Rough hands grabbed her by the arms.

'Thank Christ you're safe!'

She knew who it was before she looked up. She felt so upset about the milkman and his horse that she nearly fell against him and wept. But one did not cry in the street. 50

Extract from *Blitzcat* by Robert Westall

Underline the correct answers.

1 What had Mrs Smiley been doing?

(cleaning the silver, laying the table, feeding the cat)

2 What were the little silver mushrooms?

(ornaments she had been cleaning, a type of fungi, bullets)

2

Answer these questions.

3–6 In your own words, describe what the story is about. Use three pieces of evidence from the passage to support your answer.

_____

_____

_____

_____

7 Why was Mrs Smiley 'unable to move' (line 9)?

_____

8 Identify a **simile** in the first half of the passage.

_____

9 What does the word 'pitted' mean in line 37?

_____

10 Mrs Smiley yelled at her cat on line 7, yet a little while later was worried about where the cat was. Why do you think she reacted like this?

_____

11 Copy the line that shows that Mrs Smiley had been in danger.

_____

12 There is a sentence in this passage that highlights to the reader that despite everything, 'life goes on'. Which sentence is this?

_____

13–15 Describe the way that Mrs Smiley reacts to the situation she finds herself in. Include two pieces of evidence from the passage to support your answer.

_____

_____

_____

13

D 11

Write the **root word** in each word.

16 signature _____   **17** hopefully _____

18 statement _____   **19** doubtful _____

20	decoration	_____	21	laziness	_____
22	instantaneous	_____	23	extension	_____

8

D 5

Add the missing apostrophes.

24–25 Im sorry were going to be late.

26 Liz fed Aimees ducks.

27 Wheres the party?

28 The dogs coats were muddy and wet.

29–31 Lets hide Jakes homework here, hell never find it.

8

D 6

In each space write an appropriate **preposition**.

32 Mrs Griffiths sat _____ Nina and Tahir to stop them talking.

33 Laith hid _____ the stage curtains, afraid to go on.

34 I stood _____ the platform waiting for the train.

35 The deer ran back _____ the woods.

36 If you keep rolling sweets _____ your mouth they dissolve slowly.

37 The keys fell _____ the radiator and the wall.

38 Lucy got dressed _____ her insect costume, ready for the party.

7

Write the feminine of each of these words.

39	baron	_____	40	nephew	_____
41	billy-goat	_____	42	drake	_____
43	duke	_____	44	stag	_____

6

D 2

Write an **adjectival phrase** about each of these **nouns**.

45 a horse _____

46 the moon _____

47 a film _____

48 the wind _____

4

Rewrite each word, adding the missing silent letter so that each word is spelt correctly.

E 2

49 autum   _____

50 kichen   _____

51 hankerchief   _____

52 sutlety   _____

53 salm   _____

54 sience   _____

55 rench   _____

56 colum   _____

8

Write these words in reverse **alphabetical order**.

inseparable   insinuate   insistent   inscription   insincere   insensitive

57 (1) _____

58 (2) _____

59 (3) _____

60 (4) _____

61 (5) _____

62 (6) _____

6

Rewrite the passage, separating the words correctly and adding the missing capital letters and punctuation.

D 5

63–89

whoistherecriedstevenputtinghisheadoutofhisbedroomwindowitsmikestevenwhatdoyou

wantheaskedsadiehasfallenfromtheswingscanyouaskyourdadtocomeasquicklyas

possiblesheneedsadoctortocheckherleg

_____

_____

_____

_____

_____

_____

_____

_____

27

Add the missing commas to these sentences.

90–91 Every afternoon, as they were coming home from school, Mina and Toby used to play by the banks of the river.

92 It was a lovely, large garden with soft green grass.

93–94 High above, the city on a tall column, stood the statue of Nelson.

Write two words that begin with each of these hyphenated **prefixes**.

95–96 off-   _____ _____

97–98 over-   _____ _____

99–100 re-   _____ _____

Now go to the Progress Chart to record your score!   Total   10C

Progress Chart   English 10–11+ years Book 2

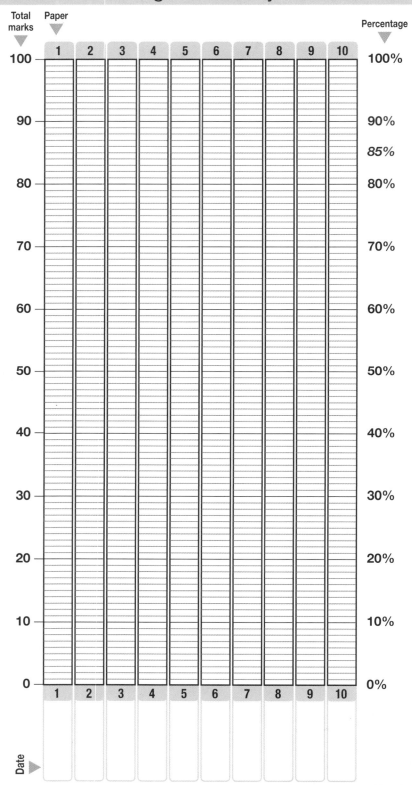

When you've finished the book use the Next Step Planner